COLLE
BRITISH
STAMPS

A STANLEY GIBBONS CHECKLIST OF
THE STAMPS OF GREAT BRITAIN

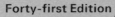

Forty-first Edition

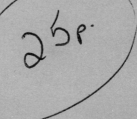

25p.

STANLEY GIBBONS PUBLICATIONS LTD

By Appointment to H. M. the Queen
Stanley Gibbons Ltd, London Philatelists.

London and Ringwood

COLLECT BRITISH STAMPS

The 41st Edition

From the famous Penny Black of 1840 to the absorbing issues of today, the stamps of Great Britain are highly popular with collectors. *Collect British Stamps* has been our message since very early days – but particularly since the First Edition of this checklist in September 1967. This 41st edition includes all the recent issues. Prices have been carefully revised to reflect today's market. Total sales of *Collect British Stamps* are now over $3\frac{1}{4}$ million copies.

Collect British Stamps appears in the autumn of each year. A more detailed Great Britain catalogue, the *Concise*, is published each spring. The *Concise* incorporates many additional listings covering watermark varieties, phosphor omitted errors, missing colour errors, stamp booklets and special commemorative First Day Cover postmarks. It is ideally suited for the collector who wishes to discover more about GB stamps.

Listings in this edition of *Collect British Stamps* include all 1989 issues which have appeared up to the publication date.

Scope. *Collect British Stamps* comprises:
- All stamps with different watermark (*wmk*) or perforation (*perf*).
- Visible plate numbers on the Victorian issues.
- Graphite-lined and phosphor issues, including variations in the number of phosphor bands.
- First Day Covers for all Special Issues.
- Special Sections for Definitive and Regional First Day Covers of the present reign.
- Presentation, Gift and Souvenir Packs.
- Post Office Yearbooks.
- Regional issues and War Occupation stamps of Guernsey and Jersey.
- Postage Due and Official Stamps.
- Post Office Picture Cards (PHO cards).
- Commemorative gutter pairs and "Traffic Light" gutter pairs listed as mint sets.
- Royal Mail Postage Labels priced as sets and on P.O. First Day Cover.

Stamps of the independent postal administrations of Guernsey, Isle of Man and Jersey ar contained in *Collect Channel Islands and Isle o Man Stamps*.

Layout. Stamps are set out chronologically b date of issue. In the catalogue lists the firs numeral is the Stanley Gibbons catalogu number; the black (boldface) numeral alongsid is the type number referring to the respectiv illustration. A blank in this column implies tha the number immediately above is repeated. Th denomination and colour of the stamp are the shown. Before February 1971 British currenc was:

£1 = 20s	One pound = twenty shillings *an*
1s = 12d	One shilling = twelve pence.

Upon decimalisation this became:

£1 = 100p	One pound = one hundred (new pence.

The catalogue list then shows two pric columns. The left-hand is for unused stamps ar the right-hand for used. Corresponding sma boxes are provided in which collectors may wis to check off the items in their collection.

Our method of indicating prices is:
Numerals for pence, e.g. 5 denotes 5p (5 pence
Numerals for pounds and pence, e.g. 4·2 denotes £4·25 (4 pounds and 25 pence).
For £100 and above, prices are in whole pound and so include the £ sign and omit the zeros f pence.

Colour illustrations. The colour illustratio of stamps are intended as a guide only; they ma differ in shade from the originals.

Size of illustrations. To comply with Po Office regulations stamp illustrations are thre quarters linear size. Separate illustrations of su charges, overprints and watermarks are actu size.

Prices. Prices quoted in this catalogue are o selling prices at the time the book went to pres They are for stamps in fine condition; in issu where condition varies we may ask more for th uperb and less for the sub-standard. The nused prices for stamps of Queen Victoria to (ing Edward VIII are for lightly hinged examples. Jnused prices for King George VI and Queen lizabeth II are for unmounted mint (though vhen not available unmounted, mounted stamps re often supplied at a lower price). Prices for sed stamps refer to postally used copies. All rices are subject to change without prior notice nd we give no guarantee to supply all stamps riced, since it is not possible to keep every atalogued item in stock. Commemorative issues 1ay, at times, only be available in complete sets nd not as individual values.

In the price columns:
=Does not exist.
—) or blank=Exists, or may exist, but price cannot be quoted.
=Not normally issued (the so-called 'Abnormals' of 1862–80).

'erforations. The 'perforation' is the number of oles in a length of 2 cm, as measured by the ibbons *Instanta* gauge. The stamp is viewed gainst a dark background with the transparent auge put on top of it. Perforations are quoted to 1e nearest half. Stamps without perforation are rmed 'imperforate'.

Se-tenant block

Se-tenant combinations. *Se-tenant* means 'joined together'. Some sets include stamps of different design arranged *se-tenant* as blocks or strips and these are often collected unsevered as issued. Where such combinations exist the stamps are priced both mint and used, as singles or complete combinations. The set price for mint refers to the unsevered combination plus singles of any other values in the set. The used set price is for single stamps of all values.

First day covers. Prices for first day covers are for complete sets used on plain covers (1924, 1925, 1929) or on special covers (1935 onwards), the stamps of which are cancelled with ordinary operational postmarks (1924–1962) or by the *standard* "First Day of Issue" postmarks (1963 onwards). Where the stamps in a set were issued on different days, prices are for a cover from each day.

PHQ cards. Since 1973 the Post Office has produced a series of picture cards, which can be sent through the post as postcards. Each card shows an enlarged colour reproduction of a current British stamp, either of one or more values from a set or of all values. Cards are priced here in fine mint condition for sets complete as issued. The Post Office gives each card a 'PHQ' serial number, hence the term. The cards are usually on sale shortly before the date of issue of the stamps, but there is no officially designated 'first day'.

Used prices are for cards franked with the stamp depicted, on the obverse or reverse; the stamp being cancelled with an official postmark for first day of issue.

Gutter pairs. All modern Great Britain commemoratives are produced in sheets containing two panes of stamps separated by a blank horizontal or vertical margin known as a gutter. This feature first made its appearance on some supplies of the 1972 Royal Silver Wedding 3p, and marked the introduction of Harrison & Sons' new "Jumelle" stamp-printing press. There are advantages for both the printer and the Post

Office in such a layout which has now been used for all commemorative issues since 1974.

The term "gutter pair" is used for a pair of stamps separated by part of the blank gutter margin.

Gutter pair

Most printers include some form of colour check device on the sheet margins, in addition to the cylinder or plate numbers. Harrison & Sons use round "dabs", or spots of colour, resembling traffic lights. For the period from the 1972 Royal Silver Wedding until the end of 1979 these colour dabs appeared in the gutter margin. Gutter pairs showing these "traffic lights" are worth considerably more than the normal version.

Traffic light gutter pair

Catalogue numbers used. The checklist uses the same catalogue numbers as the Stanley Gibbons *British Commonwealth* Catalogue (Part 1), 1990 edition.

Latest issue date for stamps recorded in this edition is 14 November 1989.

STANLEY GIBBONS LTD

Head Office: 399 Strand, London WC2R 0LX
Auction Room and Specialist Stamp Departments—Open Monday-Friday 9.30 a.m. to 5 p.m.
Shop—Open Monday–Friday 9.30 a.m. to 6.00 p.m. and Saturday 10 a.m. to 4 p.m.

Telephone 01-836 8444 and Telex 28883 for all departments

Stanley Gibbons Publications Ltd:
  Editorial, Sales Offices and
    Distribution Centre,
  5, Parkside, Christchurch Road,
  Ringwood, Hants BH24 3SH.
  Telephone 0425 472363

ISBN: 0-85259-229-9
© Stanley Gibbons Publications Ltd 1989

Printed in Great Britain by Jolly & Barber Ltd, Rugby, Warwickshire

QUEEN VICTORIA

1837 (20 June)–1901 (22 Jan.)

IDENTIFICATION. In this checklist Victorian stamps are classified firstly according to which printing method was used – line-engraving, embossing or surface-printing.

Corner letters. Numerous stamps also have letters in all four, or just the lower, corners. These were an anti-forgery device and the letters differ from stamp to stamp. If present in all four corners the upper pair are the reverse of the lower. Note the importance of these corner letters in the way the checklist is arranged.

Watermarks. Further classification depends on watermarks: these are illustrated in normal position, with stamps priced accordingly.

1 Line-engraved Issues

1

1a

2

2a White lines added above and below head

3 Small Crown watermark

4 Large Crown watermark

Letters in lower corners

1840 *Wmk Small Crown Type* **3** *Imperforate*

Cat. No.	Type				Unused	Used		
2	1	1d black	..	..	£2750	£140	☐	☐
5	2	2d blue	..	..	£5500	£300	☐	☐

1841

8	1a	1d red-brown	..		£125	3·00	☐	☐
4	2a	2d blue	..	..	£1000	30·00	☐	☐

1854–57 (i) *Wmk Small Crown Type* **3** *Perf* 16

17	1a	1d red-brown	..	..	£120	3·00	☐	☐
19	2a	2d blue			£1250	35·00	☐	☐

(ii) *Wmk Small Crown Type* **3** *Perf* 14

24a	1a	1d red-brown			£225	18·00	☐	☐
23a	2a	2d blue	..	..	£1750	£110	☐	☐

(iii) *Wmk Large Crown Type* **4** *Perf* 16

26	1a	1d red	..	..	£400	28·00	☐	☐
27	2a	2d blue	..	..	£2000	£125	☐	☐

(iv) *Wmk Large Crown Type* **4** *Perf* 14

40	1a	1d red	..	..	25·00	60	☐	☐
34	2a	2d blue	..	..	£1000	22·00	☐	☐

5

6 Watermark extending over three stamps

7

8

9

Letters in all four corners

Plate numbers. Stamps included a 'plate number' in their design and this affects valuation. The cheapest plates are priced here; see complete list of plate numbers overleaf.

1858–70 (i) *Wmk Type* **6** *Perf* 14

48	5	½d red	..	..	40·00	5·00	☐	☐

(ii) *Wmk Large Crown Type* **4** *Perf* 14

43	7	1d red	..	..	9·00	60	☐	☐
51	8	1½d red	..	..	£150	16·00	☐	☐
45	9	2d blue	..	..	£150	2·50	☐	☐

PLATE NUMBERS
on stamps of 1858–70 having letters in all four corners

Positions of Plate Numbers

Shows
Plate 9 (½d)

Shows
Plate 170 (1d, 2d)

Shows
Plate 3 (1½d)

HALFPENNY VALUE (S.G. 48)

Plate	Un.	Used			Plate	Un.	Used	
1	90·00	35·00	☐	☐	11	40·00	5·00	☐
3	55·00	14·00	☐	☐	12	40·00	5·00	☐
4	70·00	7·00	☐	☐	13	40·00	5·00	☐
5	50·00	5·00	☐	☐	14	40·00	5·00	☐
6	40·00	5·00	☐	☐	15	55·00	9·00	☐
8	80·00	35·00	☐	☐	19	85·00	18·00	☐
9	£2000	£300	☐	☐	20	90·00	30·00	☐
10	70·00	5·00	☐	☐				

Plates 2, 7, 16, 17 and 18 were not completed, while Plates 21 and 2
though made, were not used. Plate 9 was a reserve plate, not greatly use

PENNY VALUE (S.G. 43)

Plate	Un.	Used			Plate	Un.	Used			Plate	Un.	Used			Plate	Un.	Used	
71	22·00	3·00	☐	☐	112	60·00	1·50	☐	☑	154	15·00	60	☐	☐	190	10·00	5·00	☐
72	35·00	3·50	☐	☑	113	15·00	11·00	☐	☐	155	16·00	1·00	☐	☑	191	9·00	6·00	☐
73	25·00	3·00	☐	☑	114	£350	12·00	☐	☐	156	15·00	75	☐	☐	192	25·00	75	☐
74	20·00	75	☐	☑	115	£100	1·50	☐	☐	157	15·00	75	☐	☐	193	9·00	75	☐
76	40·00	75	☐	☑	116	75·00	9·00	☐	☐	158	9·00	75	☐	☐	194	15·00	7·00	☐
77	£50000	£30000	☐	☐	117	16·00	60	☐	☐	159	9·00	75	☐	☐	195	15·00	7·00	☐
78	£100	75	☐	☑	118	25·00	75	☐	☐	160	9·00	60	☐	☐	196	10·00	4·00	☐
79	30·00	60	☐	☐	119	10·00	1·00	☐	☐	161	29·00	6·00	☐	☐	197	16·00	12·00	☐
80	20·00	1·25	☐	☑	120	9·00	60	☐	☐	162	16·00	6·00	☐	☐	198	9·00	5·00	☐
81	60·00	1·50	☐	☑	121	40·00	9·00	☐	☐	163	15·00	2·00	☐	☑	199	20·00	5·00	☐
82	£120	3·50	☐	☐	122	9·00	60	☐	☐	164	15·00	3·00	☐	☐	200	20·00	75	☐
83	£140	6·00	☐	☐	123	12·00	1·00	☐	☑	165	20·00	75	☐	☐	201	9·00	6·00	☐
84	60·00	1·50	☐	☑	124	12·00	60	☐	☐	166	15·00	5·00	☐	☐	202	15·00	7·00	☐
85	25·00	1·50	☐	☐	125	15·00	2·00	☐	☐	167	10·00	70	☐	☑	203	9·00	15·00	☐
86	30·00	3·50	☐	☑	127	35·00	2·00	☐	☐	168	12·00	7·00	☐	☑	204	12·00	1·00	☐
87	9·00	1·00	☐	☑	129	11·00	7·00	☐	☑	169	30·00	6·00	☐	☐	205	11·00	3·00	☐
88	£160	8·00	☐	☐	130	18·00	1·50	☐	☐	170	11·00	60	☐	☐	206	11·00	11·00	☐
89	40·00	75	☐	☐	131	75·00	16·00	☐	☐	171	9·00	60	☐	☑	207	12·00	12·00	☐
90	28·00	75	☐	☐	132	£100	24·00	☐	☑	172	9·00	1·25	☐	☐	208	11·00	15·00	☐
91	40·00	5·00	☐	☐	133	90·00	9·00	☐	☐	173	50·00	9·00	☐	☐	209	15·00	12·00	☐
92	15·00	75	☐	☑	134	9·00	60	☐	☐	174	9·00	60	☐	☑	210	20·00	18·00	☐
93	40·00	75	☐	☐	135	£100	30·00	☐	☐	175	35·00	2·50	☐	☐	211	42·00	25·00	☐
94	40·00	4·00	☐	☐	136	£100	20·00	☐	☐	176	25·00	1·25	☐	☐	212	15·00	15·00	☐
95	25·00	75	☐	☐	137	15·00	1·25	☐	☑	177	10·00	75	☐	☑	213	15·00	15·00	☐
96	28·00	60	☐	☐	138	9·00	60	☐	☐	178	15·00	3·00	☐	☐	214	25·00	25·00	☐
97	15·00	2·50	☐	☐	139	20·00	16·00	☐	☐	179	16·00	1·50	☐	☑	215	25·00	25·00	☐
98	15·00	5·00	☐	☑	140	9·00	60	☐	☐	180	16·00	4·00	☐	☑	216	25·00	25·00	☐
99	25·00	4·00	☐	☐	141	£150	9·00	☐	☐	181	15·00	75	☐	☑	217	15·00	5·00	☐
100	35·00	1·75	☐	☑	142	50·00	25·00	☐	☐	182	£100	4·00	☐	☑	218	11·00	7·00	☐
101	50·00	8·00	☐	☐	143	30·00	15·00	☐	☐	183	25·00	2·00	☐	☐	219	60·00	75·00	☐
102	20·00	80	☐	☐	144	£100	20·00	☐	☐	184	9·00	1·00	☐	☐	220	9·00	7·00	☐
103	19·00	2·00	☐	☑	145	9·00	1·50	☐	☑	185	15·00	2·00	☐	☐	221	29·00	20·00	☐
104	28·00	4·00	☐	☐	146	10·00	5·00	☐	☐	186	30·00	1·50	☐	☐	222	35·00	40·00	☐
105	65·00	6·00	☐	☑	147	18·00	3·00	☐	☑	187	11·00	75	☐	☐	223	50·00	70·00	☐
106	30·00	80	☐	☑	148	20·00	2·50	☐	☐	188	20·00	10·00	☐	☐	224	65·00	65·00	☐
107	40·00	5·50	☐	☑	149	15·00	5·00	☐	☑	189	35·00	6·00	☐	☐	225	£1500	£400	☐
108	30·00	1·50	☐	☐	150	9·00	60	☐	☐									
109	75·00	2·50	☐	☐	151	25·00	9·00	☐	☐									
110	19·00	8·00	☐	☑	152	18·00	4·50	☐	☐									
111	35·00	1·50	☐	☐	153	70·00	8·00	☐	☐									

Plates 69, 70, 75, 77, 126 and 128 were prepared but rejected. No stam
therefore exist, except for a very few from Plate 77 which someho
reached the public. Plate 177 stamps, by accident or design, a
sometimes passed off as the rare Plate 77.

THREE-HALFPENNY VALUE (S.G. 51)

Plate	Un.	Used			Plate	Un.	Used		
(1)	£350	20·00	☐	☐	3	£150	16·00	☐	☐

Plate 1 did *not* have the plate number in the design. Plate 2 was not
completed and no stamps exist.

TWOPENNY VALUE (S.G. 45)

Plate	Un.	Used			Plate	Un.	Used	
7	£400	15·00	☐	☐	13	£175	5·50	☐
8	£450	11·00	☐	☐	14	£200	7·50	☐
9	£150	2·50	☐	☐	15	£150	7·50	☐
12	£700	40·00	☐	☐				

Plates 10 and 11 were prepared but rejected.

Embossed Issues

rices are for stamps cut square and with average to fine
mbossing. Stamps with exceptionally clear embossing are
vorth more.

11

12

13

1847–54 *Wmk 13 (6d), no wmk (others)* *Imperforate*

9	10	6d lilac	..	..	£2500	£375	☐ ☐
7	11	10d brown	..	..	£2250	£550	☐ ☐
4	12	1s green	..	..	£2750	£350	☐ ☐

Surface-printed Issues

DENTIFICATION. Check first whether the design includes
orner letters or not, as mentioned for 'Line-engraved
ssues'. The checklist is divided up according to whether any
tters are small or large, also whether they are white
uncoloured) or printed in the colour of the stamp. Further
dentification then depends on watermark.

ERFORATION. Except for Nos. 126/9 all the following
ssues of Queen Victoria are perf 14.

14

Small Garter

16 Medium Garter

17 Large Garter

18

19

20 Emblems

No corner letters

1855–57 (*i*) *Wmk Small Garter Type* **15**

62	14	4d red	..	..	£2250	£150	☐ ☐

(*ii*) *Wmk Medium Garter Type* **16**

64	14	4d red	..	..	£1750	£130	☐ ☐

(*iii*) *Wmk Large Garter Type* **17**

66a	14	4d red	..	..	£600	35·00	☐ ☐

(*iv*) *Wmk Emblems Type* **20**

70	18	6d lilac	..	..	£500	35·00	☐ ☐
73	19	1s green	..	..	£600	£100	☐ ☐

Plate numbers. Stamps Nos. 90/163 should be checked
for the 'plate numbers' indicated, as this affects valuation (the
cheapest plates are priced here). The mark '*Pl.*' shows that
several numbers exist, priced in a separate list overleaf.

Plate numbers are the small numerals appearing in duplicate
in some part of the frame design or adjacent to the lower corner
letters (in the 5s value a single numeral above the lower
inscription).

21

22

23

24

25

Small white corner letters

1862–64 *Wmk Emblems Type* **20**, *except* 4d (*Large Garter Type* **17**)

76	21	3d red	..	..	£700	£100	☐ ☐
80	22	4d red	..	..	£500	30·00	☐ ☐
84	23	6d lilac	..	..	£650	28·00	☐ ☐
86	24	9d bistre	..	..	£1100	£140	☐ ☐
90	25	1s green *Pl.*	..	..	£700	60·00	☐ ☐

26

27

28 (hyphen in SIX-PENCE)

32

33 Spray of Rose

34

29

30

31

Large white corner letters

1865–67 *Wmk Emblems Type* **20**, *except 4d* (*Large Garter Type* **17**)

92	**26**	3d red (Plate 4) ..	£375	35·00	☐ ☐
94	**27**	4d vermilion *Pl.*	£225	15·00	☐ ☐
97	**28**	6d lilac *Pl.* ..	£350	28·00	☐ ☐
98	**29**	9d straw *Pl.* ..	£700	£170	☐ ☐
99	**30**	10d brown (Plate 1)	†	£12000	☐
101	**31**	1s green (Plate 4)	£650	60·00	☐ ☐

1867–80 *Wmk Spray of Rose Type* **33**

103	**26**	3d red *Pl.*	£200	12·00	☐
104	**28**	6d lilac (with hyphen) (Plate 6)	£550	30·00	☐
109		6d mauve (without hyphen) *Pl.*	£275	25·00	☐
111	**29**	9d straw (Plate 4)	£600	90·00	☐
112	**30**	10d brown *Pl.* ..	£1000	£120	☐
117	**31**	1s green *Pl.*	£350	10·00	☐
119	**32**	2s blue *Pl.* ..	£950	55·00	☐
121		2s brown (Plate 1)	£6000	£900	☐

1872–73 *Wmk Spray of Rose Type* **33**

123	**34**	6d brown *Pl.* ..	£350	18·00	☐
125		6d grey (Plate 12)	£600	70·00	☐

PLATE NUMBERS
on stamps
of 1862–83

Cat. No.		Plate No.	Un.	Used	

Small White Corner Letters (1862–64)

90	1s green	2	£700	60·00	☐ ☐
		3	£11000		☐ ☐

Plate 2 is actually numbered as '1' and Plate 3 as '2' on the stamps.

Large White Corner Letters (1865–83)

103	3d red	4	£300	50·00	☐ ☐
		5	£200	14·00	☐ ☐
		6	£225	12·00	☐ ☐
		7	£275	15·00	☐ ☐
		8	£250	14·00	☐ ☐
		9	£250	18·00	☐ ☐
		10	£275	40·00	☐ ☐
94	4d verm	7	£300	19·00	☐ ☐
		8	£250	19·00	☐ ☐
		9	£250	15·00	☐ ☐
		10	£300	26·00	☐ ☐
		11	£250	15·00	☐ ☐
		12	£225	15·00	☐ ☐
		13	£250	17·00	☐ ☐
		14	£300	30·00	☐ ☐
97	6d lilac	5	£350	28·00	☐ ☐
		6	£1000	55·00	☐ ☐
109	6d mauve	8	£275	25·00	☐ ☐
		9	£275	25·00	☐ ☐
		10	*	£12000	☐ ☐
123	6d brown	11	£350	18·00	☐ ☐
		12	£750	50·00	☐ ☐

98	9d straw	4	£700	£170	☐ ☐
		5	£10000	*	☐ ☐
112	10d brown	1	£1000	£120	☐ ☐
		2	£12000	£2500	☐ ☐
117	1s green	4	£350	15·00	☐ ☐
		5	£400	12·00	☐ ☐
		6	£525	10·00	☐ ☐
		7	£525	25·00	☐ ☐
119	2s blue	1	£950	55·00	☐ ☐
		3	*	£3000	☐ ☐
126	5s red	1	£2500	£225	☐ ☐
		2	£3500	£300	☐ ☐

Large Coloured Corner Letters (1873–83)

139	2½d mauve	1	£225	25·00	☐ ☐
		2	£225	25·00	☐ ☐
		3	£400	30·00	☐ ☐
141	2½d mauve	3	£500	30·00	☐ ☐
		4	£200	12·00	☐ ☐
		5	£200	16·00	☐ ☐
		6	£200	12·00	☐ ☐
		7	£200	12·00	☐ ☐
		8	£200	16·00	☐ ☐
		9	£200	12·00	☐ ☐
		10	£225	17·00	☐ ☐
		11	£200	12·00	☐ ☐
		12	£200	16·00	☐ ☐
		13	£200	16·00	☐ ☐
		14	£200	12·00	☐ ☐
		15	£200	12·00	☐ ☐
		16	£200	12·00	☐ ☐
		17	£550	80·00	☐ ☐
142	2½d blue	17	£175	20·00	☐ ☐
		18	£200	12·00	☐ ☐
		19	£175	10·00	☐ ☐
		20	£175	10·00	☐ ☐

157	2½d blue	21	£225	9·00	☐
		22	£175	8·00	☐
		23	£175	8·00	☐
143	3d red	11	£200	12·00	☐
		12	£225	14·00	☐
		14	£250	15·00	☐
		15	£200	14·00	☐
		16	£200	14·00	☐
		17	£225	14·00	☐
		18	£225	14·00	☐
		19	£200	14·00	☐
		20	£200	30·00	☐
158	3d red	20	£225	35·00	☐
		21	£180	25·00	☐
152	4d verm	15	£600	£140	☐
		16	*	£10000	☐
153	4d green	15	£450	90·00	☐
		16	£400	85·00	☐
160	4d brown	17	*	£6000	☐
		17	£175	25·00	☐
		18	£175	25·00	☐
147	6d grey	13	£225	18·00	☐
		14	£225	18·00	☐
		15	£225	16·00	☐
		16	£225	16·00	☐
		17	£300	35·00	☐
161	6d grey	17	£180	20·00	☐
		18	£150	20·00	☐
150	1s green	8	£325	32·00	☐
		9	£325	32·00	☐
		10	£300	32·00	☐
		11	£300	32·00	☐
		12	£250	26·00	☐
		13	£250	26·00	☐
		14	*	£10000	☐
163	1s brown	13	£275	40·00	☐
		14	£225	40·00	☐

4

35

36

44

45

46

37

47 Small Anchor

48 Orb

Large coloured corner letters

1873–80 (i) *Wmk Small Anchor Type* **47**

139	**41**	2½d mauve *Pl.*	..	£225	25·00	☐ ☐

(ii) *Wmk Orb Type* **48**

141	**41**	2½d mauve *Pl.*	..	£200	12·00	☐ ☐
142		2½d blue *Pl.*	..	£175	10·00	☐ ☐

(iii) *Wmk Spray of Rose Type* **33**

143	**42**	3d red *Pl.*	..	£200	12·00	☐ ☐
145	**43**	6d pale buff				☐ ☐
		(Plate 13)	•	£4500		☐ ☐
147		6d grey *Pl.*	..	£225	16·00	☐ ☐
150	**44**	1s green *Pl.*	..	£250	26·00	☐ ☐
151		1s brown (Plate 13)	£1100	£150		☐ ☐

(iv) *Wmk Large Garter Type* **17**

152	**45**	4d vermilion *Pl.*	..	£600	£140	☐ ☐
153		4d green *Pl.*	..	£400	85·00	☐ ☐
154		4d brown (Plate 17)	£600	£120		☐ ☐
156	**46**	8d orange (Plate 1)	£550	£100		☐ ☐

38

39 Maltese Cross   40 Large Anchor

1867–83 (i) *Wmk Maltese Cross Type* **39**   *Perf* 15½×15

126	**35**	5s red *Pl.*	.. ..	£2500	£225	☐ ☐
128	**36**	10s grey (Plate 1)	..	£18000	£800	☐ ☐
129	**37**	£1 brown (Plate 1)	£22000	£1100		☐ ☐

(ii) *Wmk Large Anchor Type* **40**   *Perf* 14

134	**35**	5s red (Plate 4)	..	£4500	£800	☐ ☐
131	**36**	10s grey (Plate 1)	..	£20000	£1000	☐ ☐
132	**37**	£1 brown (Plate 1)	£27000	£2000		☐ ☐
137	**38**	£5 orange (Plate 1)	£4000	£1200		☐ ☐

49 Imperial Crown   (**50**) Surcharges in red (**51**)

1880–83 *Wmk Imperial Crown Type* **49**

157	**41**	2½d blue *Pl.*	..	£175	8·00	☐ ☐
158	**42**	3d red *Pl.*	.. ..	£180	25·00	☐ ☐
159		3d on 3d lilac				
		(surch Type **50**)	£225	60·00		☐ ☐
160	**45**	4d brown *Pl.*	..	£175	25·00	☐ ☐
161	**43**	6d grey *Pl.*	..	£150	20·00	☐ ☐
162		6d on 6d lilac				
		(surch Type **51**)	£200	60·00		☐ ☐
163	**44**	1s brown *Pl.*	..	£225	40·00	☐ ☐

41

42

43

52   53   54

55   56

1880–81 *Wmk Imperial Crown Type* 49

164	52	½d green	..	..	15·00	2·50	☐	☐
166	53	1d brown	..	..	4·00	1·25	☐	☐
167	54	1½d brown	..	..	70·00	14·00	☐	☐
168	55	2d red ..	..	..	75·00	25·00	☐	☐
169	56	5d indigo	..	..	£350	35·00	☐	☐

57   Die I   Die II

1881 *Wmk Imperial Crown Type* 49
(*a*) 14 *dots in each corner, Die* I

| 171 | 57 | 1d lilac | .. | .. | 75·00 | 12·00 | ☐ | ☐ |

(*b*) 16 *dots in each corner, Die* II

| 173 | 57 | 1d lilac | .. | .. | 1·00 | 30 | ☐ | ☐ |

58   59

60

Coloured letters in the corners

1883-84 *Wmk Anchor Type* 40

179	58	2s 6d deep lilac	..	..	£200	50·00	☐	☐
181	59	5s red	..	..	£400	60·00	☐	☐
183	60	10s blue ..	..	..	£700	£200	☐	☐

61

1884 *Wmk 3 Imperial Crowns Type* 49

| 185 | 61 | £1 brown | .. | .. | £9000 | £800 | ☐ | ☐ |

1888 *Wmk 3 Orbs Type* 48

| 186 | 61 | £1 brown | .. | .. | £16000 | £1200 | ☐ | ☐ |

1891 *Wmk 3 Imperial Crowns Type* 49

| 212 | 61 | £1 green | .. | .. | £2000 | £350 | ☐ | ☐ |

62   63   64

65   66

1883–84 *Wmk Imperial Crown Type* 49 (*sideways on horiz designs*)

187	52	½d blue	..	..	8·00	1·50	☐	☐
188	62	1½d lilac	..	..	55·00	18·00	☐	☐
189	63	2d lilac	..	..	70·00	25·00	☐	☐
190	64	2½d lilac	..	..	40·00	5·00	☐	☐
191	.65	3d lilac	..	..	90·00	40·00	☐	☐
192	66	4d dull green	..	..	£200	70·00	☐	☐
193	62	5d dull green	..	..	£200	70·00	☐	☐
194	63	6d dull green	..	..	£225	80·00	☐	☐
195	64	9d dull green	..	..	£475	£200	☐	☐
196	65	1s dull green	..	..	£350	£120	☐	☐

The above prices are for stamps in the true dull gree
colour. Stamps which have been soaked, causing the colou
to run, are virtually worthless.

6

67

68

69

70

71

72

73

74

75

76

77

78

79

80

81

82

83

84

85

86

87

88

89

'Jubilee' issue

1887–1900 *The bicoloured stamps have the value tablets, or the frames including the value tablets, in the second colour. Wmk Imperial Crown Type* **49**

197	67	½d	vermilion	..	75	30	☐ ☐
213		½d	green*	.. ..	1·00	40	☐ ☐
198	68	1½d	purple and green		8·00	2·00	☐ ☐
200	69	2d	green and red ..		13·00	4·00	☐ ☐
201	70	2½d	purple on blue		8·00	40	☐ ☐
203	71	3d	purple on yellow		13·00	1·00	☐ ☐
205a	72	4d	green and brown		16·00	6·00	☐ ☐
206	73	4½d	green and red ..		3·75	20·00	☐ ☐
207a	74	5d	purple and blue		18·00	3·50	☐ ☐
208	75	6d	purple on red ..		18·00	5·00	☐ ☐
209	76	9d	purple and blue		40·00	25·00	☐ ☐
210	77	10d	purple and red		35·00	22·00	☐ ☐
211	78	1s	green	.. ..	£125	30·00	☐ ☐
214		1s	green and red ..		45·00	70·00	☐ ☐
	Set of 14		.. .. ..		£300	£170	☐ ☐

The ½d, No. 213, in blue, has had the colour changed due to exposure to moisture.

90

91

92

93

(a) *Perf* 14

215	79	½d blue-green ..	60	30	□	□
217		½d yellow-green ..	50	20	□	□
219		1d red ..	50	15	□	□
222	80	1½d purple and green	12·00	4·75	□	□
291	81	2d green and red ..	10·00	4·50	□	□
231	82	2½d blue ..	4·50	2·50	□	□
234	83	3d purple on yellow	13·00	6·00	□	□
237	84	4d green and brown	22·00	7·00	□	□
240		4d orange	7·50	6·50	□	□
294	85	5d purple and blue	11·00	4·75	□	□
245	79	6d purple ..	15·00	4·00	□	□
249	86	7d grey	3·50	6·00	□	□
307	87	9d purple and blue	40·00	22·00	□	□
311	88	10d purple and red ..	35·00	20·00	□	□
314	89	1s green and red ..	28·00	8·00	□	□
316	90	2s 6d lilac	£135	45·00	□	□
263	91	5s red	£200	55·00	□	□
265	92	10s blue	£475	£200	□	□
320	93	£1 green	£1100	£275	□	□
		Set of 15 (*to* 1s) ..	£180	90·00	□	□

(b) *Perf* 15×14

279	79	½d green	20·00	25·00	□	□
281		1d red	5·00	3·00	□	□
283	82	2½d blue	11·00	5·00	□	□
285	83	3d purple on yellow	18·00	3·50	□	□
286	84	4d orange	13·00	6·00	□	□
		Set of 5	60·00	35·00	□	□

KING GEORGE V
1910 (6 May)–1936 (20 Jan.)

PERFORATION. All the following issues are Perf 15×14 except vertical commemorative stamps which are 14×15, unless otherwise stated.

94 (Hair dark)   **95** (Lion unshaded)   **96**

1911–12 *Wmk Imperial Crown Type* **49**

322	94	½d green	2·25	75	□	□
327	95	1d red	2·00	90	□	□

1912 *Wmk Royal Cypher ('Simple') Type* **96**

335	94	½d green	28·00	22·00	□	□
336	95	1d red	15·00	12·00	□	□

97 (Hair light)   **98** (Lion shaded)   **99**

1912 *Wmk Imperial Crown Type* **49**

340	97	½d green	2·50	40	□	□
342	98	1d red	1·00	35	□	□

1912 *Wmk Royal Cypher ('Simple') Type* **96**

344	97	½d green	3·00	60	□	□
345	98	1d red	1·50	40	□	□

1912 *Wmk Royal Cypher ('Multiple') Type* **99**

346	97	½d green	5·00	3·00	□	□
349	98	1d red	6·50	4·00	□	□

100   **101**   **102**

103   **104**

1912–24 *Wmk Royal Cypher Type* **96**

351	101	½d green	40	12	□	□
357	100	1d red	25	15	□	□
362	101	1½d brown	80	15	□	□
368	102	2d orange	90	35	□	□
372	100	2½d blue	4·00	1·00	□	□
375	102	3d violet	2·00	55	□	□
379		4d grey-green ..	4·50	60	□	□
382	103	5d brown	4·50	2·25	□	□
385		6d purple	7·00	1·00	□	□
		a. Perf 14 ..	60·00	80·00	□	□
387		7d olive-green ..	9·00	3·75	□	□
390		8d black on yellow	20·00	6·50	□	□
392	104	9d black	7·00	2·00	□	□
393a		9d olive-green ..	65·00	14·00	□	□
394		10d blue	13·00	11·00	□	□
395		1s brown	7·50	75	□	□
		Set of 15	£130	38·00	□	□

| 97 | **101** | ½d green | .. | .. | 75·00 | 90·00 | □ | □ |
| 98 | **100** | 1d red .. | .. | .. | £150 | £130 | □ | □ |

ee also Nos. 418/29.

105

106

105. Background around portrait consists of horizontal lines

913–18 *Wmk Single Cypher Type* **106** *Perf* 11 × 12

13a	**105**	2s 6d brown	..	..	70·00	25·00	□	□
16		5s red ..	..	.	£175	35·00	□	□
17		10s blue	..	..	£300	80·00	□	□
03		£1 green	..	..	£1250	£600	□	□
	Set of 4		..	..	£1600	£700	□	□

ee also Nos. 450/2.

107

924–26 *Wmk Block Cypher Type* **107**

8	**101**	½d green	..	..	12	12	□	□
9	**100**	1d red ..	..	..	25	25	□	□
0	**101**	1½d brown	..	..	20	20	□	□
1	**102**	2d orange	..	..	80	60	□	□
2	**100**	2½d blue	..	..	4·50	90	□	□
3	**102**	3d violet	..	..	5·50	60	□	□
4		4d grey-green	..	..	7·50	90	□	□
5	**103**	5d brown	..	..	17·00	1·40	□	□
6a		6d purple	..	..	2·00	35	□	□
7	**104**	9d olive-green	..	..	9·00	2·25	□	□
8		10d blue	..	..	24·00	16·00	□	□
9		1s brown	..	..	16·00	75	□	□
	Set of 12		..	..	80·00	21·00	□	□

r full information on all future British issues, collectors
ould write to the British Post Office Philatelic Bureau, 20
andon Street, Edinburgh EH3 5TT

108   109

British Empire Exhibition

1924–25 *Wmk* **107** *Perf* 14

(*a*) 23.4.24. *Dated '1924'*

430	**108**	1d red ..	..	..	2·25	6·00	□	□
431	**109**	1½d brown	..	..	4·00	11·00	□	□
	First Day Cover	..	..	..		£350		□

(*b*) 9.5.25. *Dated '1925'*

432	**108**	1d red ..	..	..	7·50	15·00	□	□
433	**109**	1½d brown	..	..	23·00	50·00	□	□
	First Day Cover	..	..	..		£1200		□

110   111   112

113 St George and the Dragon

114

Ninth Universal Postal Union Congress

1929 (10 MAY) (*a*) *Wmk* **107**

434	110	½d green	..	..	50	90	□ □
435	111	1d red ..	..	..	70	1·00	□ □
436		1½d brown	..	..	60	90	□ □
437	112	2½d blue	..	..	5·00	9·00	□ □

(*b*) *Wmk* **114** *Perf* 12

438	113	£1 black	..	..	£650	£450	□ □
434/7	*Set of 4*		..	..	6·00	11·00	□ □
434/7	*First Day Cover (4 vals.)*		..		£500	□
434/8	*First Day Cover (5 vals.)*		..		£2500	□

120

121

122

123

115

116

117

118

119

Silver Jubilee

1935 (7 MAY) *Wmk* **107**

453	120	½d green	..	..	25	20	□
454	121	1d red ..	..	..	75	90	□
455	122	1½d brown	..	..	50	20	□
456	123	2½d blue	..	..	3·00	5·50	□
		Set of 4	..	..	4·25	6·00	□
		First Day Cover	..	..		£400	□

1934–36 *Wmk* **107**

439	115	½d green	..	..	15	15	□ □
440	116	1d red ..	..	..	15	15	□ □
441	115	1½d brown	..	..	10	15	□ □
442	117	2d orange	..	..	30	30	□ □
443	116	2½d blue	..	..	1·10	60	□ □
444	117	3d violet	..	..	1·00	50	□ □
445		4d grey-green	..	..	1·50	55	□ □
446	118	5d brown	..	..	5·00	1·50	□ □
447	119	9d olive-green	..	..	9·00	1·60	□ □
448		10d blue	..	..	12·00	8·00	□ □
449		1s brown	..	..	12·00	40	□ □
		Set of 11	..	..	35·00	11·00	□ □

T 105 (*re-engraved*). *Background around portrait consists of horizontal and diagonal lines*

1934 *Wmk* **106** *Perf* 11 × 12

450	105	2s 6d brown	..	..	50·00	15·00	□ □
451		5s red ..	..	..	£100	30·00	□ □
452		10s blue	..	..	£200	40·00	□ □
		Set of 3	..	..	£300	75·00	□ □

KING EDWARD VIII
1936 (20 Jan.–10 Dec.)

124

125

1936 *Wmk* **125**

457	124	½d green	..	..	20	12	□
458		1d red ..	..	..	50	20	□
459		1½d brown	..	..	25	12	□
460		2½d blue	..	..	25	50	□
		Set of 4	..	..	90	85	□

26 King George VI
and Queen Elizabeth

127

oronation

937 (13 MAY) *Wmk* 127

61	**126**	1½d brown	..	..	40	25	□	□
		First Day Cover	..	..		28·00		□

8   129   130

ng George VI and National Emblems

937–47 *Wmk* 127

62	**128**	½d green	..	..	10	12	□	□
63		1d scarlet	..	..	10	12	□	□
64		1½d brown	..	..	20	12	□	□
65		2d orange	..	..	1·25	35	□	□
66		2½d blue	..	..	25	12	□	□
67		3d violet	..	..	5·00	60	□	□
68	**129**	4d green	..	..	35	30	□	□
69		5d brown	..	..	2·50	35	□	□
70		6d purple	..	..	1·25	25	□	□
71	**130**	7d green	..	..	4·50	35	□	□
72		8d red	..	..	5·00	40	□	□
73		9d deep green	..	..	5·00	40	□	□
74		10d blue	..	..	4·50	45	□	□
74a		11d plum	..	..	3·00	1·25	□	□
75		1s brown	..	..	5·00	25	□	□
		Set of 15	..	..	32·00	5·00	□	□

or later printings of the lower values in apparently lighter
ades and different colours, see Nos. 485/90 and 503/8.

r full information on all future British issues, collectors
ould write to the British Post Office Philatelic Bureau, 20
ndon Street, Edinburgh EH3 5TT

131 King George VI   131a

132   132a

133

1939–48 *Wmk* 133   *Perf* 14

476	**131**	2s 6d brown	..		45·00	9·00	□	□
476a		2s 6d green	..	..	10·00	90	□	□
477	**131a**	5s red	..	..	20·00	1·25	□	□
478	**132**	10s dark blue	..		£175	18·00	□	□
478a		10s bright blue	..		38·00	4·00	□	□
478b	**132a**	£1 brown	..	..	10·00	22·00	□	□
		Set of 6	..	..	£250	48·00	□	□

134 Queen Victoria and King George VI

Centenary of First Adhesive Postage Stamps

1940 (6 MAY) *Wmk* 127   *Perf* 14½×14

479	**134**	½d green	..	..	30	20	□	□
480		1d red	..	..	40	40	□	□
481		1½d brown	..	..	30	30	□	□
482		2d orange	..	..	50	40	□	□
483		2½d blue	..	..	1·90	80	□	□
484		3d violet	..	..	4·50	4·00	□	□
		Set of 6	..	..	7·00	5·50	□	□
		First Day Cover	..	..		28·00		□

Head as Nos. 462/7, but lighter background

1941–42 *Wmk* **127**

485	**128**	½d pale green	..	12	10	☐	☐
486		1d pale red		12	10	☐	☐
487		1½d pale brown	..	65	35	☐	☐
488		2d pale orange	..	50	25	☐	☐
489		2½d light blue	..	12	10	☐	☐
490		3d pale violet	..	1·60	30	☐	☐
	Set of 6	.. .. ..		2·75	1·10	☐	☐

135 Symbols of Peace and Reconstruction

136 Symbols of Peace and Reconstruction

Victory

1946 (11 JUNE) *Wmk* **127**

491	**135**	2½d blue	.. ..	12	12	☐	☐
492	**136**	3d violet	.. ..	10	10	☐	☐
	First Day Cover	.. .. ..			38·00		☐

137 King George VI and Queen Elizabeth

138 King George VI and Queen Elizabeth

Royal Silver Wedding

1948 (26 APR.) *Wmk* **127**

493	**137**	2½d blue	.. ..	20	20	☐	☐
494	**138**	£1 blue	.. ..	38·00	35·00	☐	☐
	First Day Cover	.. ..			£325		☐

1948 (10 MAY)

Stamps of 1d and 2½d showing seaweed-gathering were on sale at eight Head Post Offices elsewhere in Great Britain, but were primarily for use in the Channel Islands and are listed there (see after Regional Issues).

139 Globe and Laurel Wreath

140 'Speed'

141 Olympic Symbol

142 Winged Victory

Olympic Games

1948 (29 JULY) *Wmk* **127**

495	**139**	2½d blue	.. ..	10	10	☐	
496	**140**	3d violet	.. ..	20	20	☐	
497	**141**	6d purple	.. ..	25	20	☐	
498	**142**	1s brown	.. ..	1·25	1·00	☐	
	Set of 4	.. ..		1·60	1·25	☐	
	First Day Cover	..			30·00		☐

143 Two Hemispheres

144 U.P.U. Monument, Berne

145 Goddess Concordia, Globe and Points of Compass

146 Posthorn and Globe

75th Anniversary of Universal Postal Union

1949 (10 OCT.) *Wmk* **127**

499	**143**	2½d blue	.. ..	10	8	☐	
500	**144**	3d violet	.. ..	30	30	☐	
501	**145**	6d purple	.. ..	45	45	☐	
502	**146**	1s brown	.. ..	1·25	1·25	☐	
	Set of 4	.. ..		1·75	1·75	☐	
	First Day Cover				55·00		

950-52

03	128	½d pale orange	..	10	12	☐	☐
04		1d light blue	..	10	12	☐	☐
05		1½d pale green	..	25	30	☐	☐
06		2d pale brown	..	25	20	☐	☐
07		2½d pale red	..	20	12	☐	☐
08	129	4d light blue	..	1·40	1·10	☐	☐
	Set of 6	.. .. ..		2·00	1·75	☐	☐

47 HMS *Victory*

148 White Cliffs of Dover

49 St George and the Dragon

150 Royal Coat of Arms

951 (3 MAY) *Wmk* 133 *Perf* 11×12

09	147	2s 6d green	..	8·00	75	☐	☐
10	148	5s red ..	..	22·00	1·50	☐	☐
11	149	10s blue	..	12·00	6·00	☐	☐
12	150	£1 brown	..	25·00	16·00	☐	☐
	Set of 4	.. ..		60·00	20·00	☐	☐

151 Commerce and Prosperity

152 Festival Symbol

Festival of Britain

951 (3 MAY) *Wmk* 127

13	151	2½d red ..	..	10	8	☐	☐
14	152	4d blue	..	35	35	☐	☐
	First Day Cover ..	..		16·00		☐	

QUEEN ELIZABETH II
6 February, 1952

153 Tudor Crown

154

155

156

157

158

159

160

Queen Elizabeth II and National Emblems

1952–54 *Wmk* 153

515	154	½d orange	..	..	10	12	☐	☐
516		1d blue	..	..	20	20	☐	☐
517		1½d green	..	..	10	12	☐	☐
518		2d brown	..	..	20	15	☐	☐
519	155	2½d red ..	..	..	10	12	☐	☐
520		3d lilac	..	..	1·00	30	☐	☐
521	156	4d blue	..	..	2·50	80	☐	☐
		4½d *(See Nos. 577, 594, 609 and 616b)*						
522	157	5d brown	..	..	90	2·00	☐	☐
523		6d purple	..	..	2·50	60	☐	☐
524		7d green	..	..	8·00	3·50	☐	☐
525	158	8d magenta	..		90	60	☐	☐
526		9d bronze-green	..		12·00	3·00	☐	☐
527		10d blue	..	..	10·00	3·00	☐	☐
528		11d plum	..	..	28·00	16·00	☐	☐
529	159	1s bistre	..	..	90	40	☐	☐
530	160	1s 3d green	..	..	5·00	2·00	☐	☐
531	159	1s 6d indigo	..	..	10·00	2·25	☐	☐
		Set of 17	.. .. ..		75·00	28·00	☐	☐

See also Nos. 540/56, 561/6, 570/94 and 599/618a.
For First Day Cover prices see page 35.

161

162

163

164

Coronation

1953 (3 JUNE) *Wmk* **153**

532	**161**	2½d red	..	..	10	8	☐ ☐
533	**162**	4d blue		..	30	70	☐ ☐
534	**163**	1s 3d green	..	..	5·00	4·00	☐ ☐
535	**164**	1s 6d blue	..	..	8·00	7·00	☐ ☐
		Set of 4	..	..	12·00	10·00	☐ ☐
		First Day Cover	..	..		32·00	☐

165 St Edward's Crown

166 Carrickfergus Castle

167 Caernarvon Castle

168 Edinburgh Castle

169 Windsor Castle

1955–58 *Wmk* **165**   *Perf* 11 × 12

536	**166**	2s 6d brown	..	..	8·00	1·50	☐ ☐
537	**167**	5s red ..	..	..	40·00	3·00	☐ ☐
538	**168**	10s blue	..	..	£100	10·00	☐ ☐
539	**169**	£1 black	..	..	£125	25·00	☐ ☐
		Set of 4	..	..	£250	35·00	☐ ☐

See also Nos. 595*a*/8*a*, 759/62 and F.D.C's on page 35.

1955–58 *Wmk* **165**

540	**154**	½d orange	..	..	10	12	☐ ☐
541		1d blue	..	..	25	12	☐ ☐
542		1½d green	..	..	10	12	☐ ☐
543		2d red-brown	..		20	20	☐ ☐
543*b*		2d light red-brown			20	12	☐ ☐
544	**155**	2½d red	..	..	12	12	☐ ☐
545		3d lilac	..	..	20	15	☐ ☐
546	**156**	4d blue	..	..	1·00	40	☐ ☐
547	**157**	5d brown	..	..	4·00	2·75	☐ ☐
548*a*		6d purple	..	..	2·50	80	☐ ☐
549		7d green	..	..	30·00	7·50	☐ ☐
550	**158**	8d magenta ..		..	4·00	1·00	☐ ☐
551		9d bronze-green	..		8·00	1·50	☐ ☐
552		10d blue	..	..	5·50	1·50	☐ ☐
553		11d plum	..	..	40	1·00	☐ ☐
554	**159**	1s bistre	..	..	6·50	40	☐ ☐
555	**160**	1s 3d green	..	..	9·50	1·25	☐ ☐
556	**159**	1s 6d indigo	..	..	15·00	1·00	☐ ☐
		Set of 18	..	..	75·00	18·00	☐ ☐

170 Scout Badge and 'Rolling Hitch'

171 'Scouts coming to Britain'

172 Globe within a Compass

173

World Scout Jubilee Jamboree

1957 (1 AUG.) *Wmk* **165**

557	**170**	2½d red ..	..	..	15	10	☐
558	**171**	4d blue	..	..	50	40	☐
559	**172**	1s 3d green	..	..	5·00	5·00	☐
		Set of 3	..	..	5·00	5·00	☐
		First Day Cover	..	..		11·00	

46th Inter Parliamentary Union Conference

1957 (12 SEPT.) *Wmk* **165**

560	**173**	4d blue	..	..	80	80	☐
		First Day Cover	..	..		80·00	

Graphite-lined and Phosphor Issues

These are used in connection with automatic sorting machinery, originally experimentally at Southampton but now also operating elsewhere. In such areas these stamps were the normal issue, but from mid 1967 *all* low-value stamps bear phosphor markings.

The graphite lines were printed in black on the back, beneath the gum; two lines per stamp except for the 2d (*see below*).

174   **175** (2d only)
Stamps viewed from back)

In November 1959, phosphor bands, printed on the front, replaced the graphite. They are wider than the graphite, not easy to see, but show as broad vertical bands at certain angles to the light.

Values representing the rate for printed papers (and second class mail from 1968) have one band and others have two, three or four bands according to size and format. From 1972 onwards some commemorative stamps were printed with 'all-over' phosphor.

In the small stamps the bands are on each side with the single band at left (except where otherwise stated). In the large-size commemorative stamps the single band may be at left, centre or right varying in different issues. The bands are vertical on both horizontal and vertical designs except where otherwise stated.

See also notes on page 35.

Graphite-lined issue

1957 (19 Nov.) *Two graphite lines on the back, except 2d value, which has one line.* Wmk **165**

561	154	½d orange	..	..	20	30	☐	☐
562		1d blue			20	35	☐	☐
563		1½d green	..	..	40	1·25	☐	☐
564		2d light red-brown			2·00	1·50	☐	☐
565	155	2½d red	..	..	5·50	8·00	☐	☐
566		3d lilac	..	..	50	50	☐	☐
	Set of 6		..	..	8·00	11·00	☐	☐

See also Nos. 587/94.

For First Day Cover price see page 35.

176 Welsh Dragon

177 Flag and Games Emblem

178 Welsh Dragon

Sixth British Empire and Commonwealth Games, Cardiff

1958 (18 JULY) *Wmk* **165**

567	**176**	3d lilac	..	..	15	10	☐	☐
568	**177**	6d mauve	..	..	25	20	☐	☐
569	**178**	1s 3d green	..	..	2·25	2·00	☐	☐
	Set of 3	..	..	..	2·25	2·10	☐	☐
	First Day Cover	..	..	..		50·00		☐

179 Multiple Crowns

WATERMARK. All the following issues to No. 755 are Watermark **179** (sideways on the vertical commemorative stamps) unless otherwise stated.

1958–65 *Wmk* **179**

570	**154**	½d orange	..	..	5	10	☐	☐
571		1d blue	..	..	5	8	☐	☐
572		1½d green	..	..	5	12	☐	☐
573		2d light red-brown			5	8	☐	☐
574	**155**	2½d red	..	..	5	10	☐	☐
575		3d lilac	..	..	10	10	☐	☐
576a	**156**	4d blue			12	10	☐	☐
577		4½d brown	..	..	10	12	☐	☐
578	**157**	5d brown	..	..	20	20	☐	☐
579		6d purple	..	..	15	12	☐	☐
580		7d green	..	..	30	20	☐	☐
581	**158**	8d magenta	..	..	45	15	☐	☐
582		9d bronze-green	..		35	15	☐	☐
583		10d blue	..	..	90	15	☐	☐
584	**159**	1s bistre	..	..	30	12	☐	☐
585	**160**	1s 3d green	..	..	25	15	☐	☐
586	**159**	1s 6d indigo	..	..	4·00	40	☐	☐
	Set of 17	..	..	..	6·00	2·10	☐	☐

For 4½d on First Day Cover see page 35.

For full information on all future British issues, collectors should write to the British Post Office Philatelic Bureau, 20 Brandon Street, Edinburgh EH3 5TT

Graphite-lined issue

1958–61 Two graphite lines on the back, except 2d value, which has one line. Wmk **179**

587	154	½d orange	.. ..	2·00	3·00	☐	☐
588		1d blue	.. ..	90	1·25	☐	☐
589		1½d green	.. ..	30·00	30·00	☐	☐
590		2d light red-brown		7·00	4·00	☐	☐
591	155	2½d red ..	.. ..	10·00	10·00	☐	☐
592		3d lilac	.. ..	40	40	☐	☐
593	156	4d blue	.. ..	3·50	4·50	☐	☐
594		4½d brown	.. ..	4·00	4·00	☐	☐
		Set of 8	.. .. ..	55·00	45·00	☐	☐

The prices quoted for No. 589 are for examples with inverted watermark. Stamps with upright watermark are *priced at £85 mint, £60 used.*

1959–63 Wmk **179**   *Perf* 11 × 12

595a	166	2s 6d brown	., ..	40	30	☐	☐
596a	167	5s red ..	.. ..	1·00	60	☐	☐
597a	168	10s blue	.. ..	2·25	3·00	☐	☐
598a	169	£1 black	.. ..	9·50	5·00	☐	☐
		Set of 4	.. ..	12·00	8·00	☐	☐

Phosphor-Graphite issue

1959 (18 Nov.) Two phosphor bands on front and two graphite lines on back, except 2d value, which has one band on front and one line on back

(a) Wmk **165**

599	154	½d orange	.. ..	3·50	5·00	☐	☐
600		1d blue	.. ..	3·50	4·50	☐	☐
601		1½d green	.. ..	3·50	4·50	☐	☐

(b) Wmk **179**

605	154	2d light red-brown (1 band) ..		5·00	4·50	☐	☐
606	155	2½d red ..	.. ..	12·00	11·00	☐	☐
607		3d lilac	.. ..	11·00	7·50	☐	☐
608	156	4d blue	.. ..	6·00	27·00	☐	☐
609		4½d brown	.. ..	40·00	18·00	☐	☐
		Set of 8	.. .. ..	70·00	75·00	☐	☐

Phosphor issue

1960–67 Two phosphor bands on front, except where otherwise stated. Wmk **179**

610	154	½d orange	.. ..	8	12	☐	☐
611		1d blue	.. ..	8	10	☐	☐
612		1½d green	.. ..	10	20	☐	☐
613		2d light red-brown (1 band) ..		22·00	20·00	☐	☐
613a		2d light red-brown (2 bands)		8	10	☐	☐
614	155	2½d red (2 bands) ..		10	40	☐	☐
614a		2½d red (1 band)		40	75	☐	☐
615		3d lilac (2 bands)		45	45	☐	☐
615c		3d lilac (1 side band) ..		35	60	☐	☐
615e		3d lilac (1 centre band) ..		25	40	☐	☐

616a	156	4d blue	.. ..	12	12	☐	☐
616b		4½d brown	.. ..	12	25	☐	☐
616c	157	5d brown	.. ..	20	25	☐	☐
617		6d purple	.. ..	40	20	☐	☐
617a		7d green	.. ..	60	25	☐	☐
617b	158	8d magenta ..		20	25	☐	☐
617c		9d bronze-green ..		50	25	☐	☐
617d		10d blue	.. ..	80	35	☐	☐
617e	159	1s bistre	.. ..	40	20	☐	☐
618	160	1s 3d green	.. ..	2·00	2·50	☐	☐
618a	159	1s 6d indigo	.. ..	1·60	1·00	☐	☐
		Set of 17 (one of each value)		7·00	6·00	☐	☐

No. 615c exists with the phosphor band at the left or rig[ht] of the stamp.

180 Postboy of 1660

181 Posthorn of 1660

Tercentenary of Establishment of 'General Letter Office'

1960 (7 July)

619	180	3d lilac	.. ..	20	10	☐	
620	181	1s 3d green	.. ..	4·50	4·25	☐	
		Set of 2	.. ..	4·50	4·25	☐	
		First Day Cover ..	..		38·00		

182 Conference Emblem

First Anniversary of European Postal and Telecommunications Conference

1960 (19 Sept.)

621	182	6d green and purple		40	60	☐	
622		1s 6d brown and blue		6·50	5·50	☐	
		Set of 2	.. .. ..	6·50	5·50	☐	
		First Day Cover	.. ..		27·00		

183 Thrift Plant

184 'Growth of Savings'

185 Thrift Plant

Centenary of Post Office Savings Bank

1961 (28 Aug.)

623	**183**	2½d black and red ..	10	10	☐	☐
624	**184**	3d orange-brown				
		and violet ..	10	10	☐	☐
625	**185**	1s 6d red and blue ..	2·60	2·00	☐	☐
	Set of 3	.. ..	2·60	2·00	☐	☐
	First Day Cover	.. ..		55·00		☐

186 C.E.P.T. Emblem

187 Doves and Emblem

188 Doves and Emblem

European Postal and Telecommunications (C.E.P.T.) Conference, Torquay

1961 (18 Sept.)

626	**186**	2d orange, pink				
		and brown ..	10	10	☐	☐
627	**187**	4d buff, mauve and				
		ultramarine ..	20	10	☐	☐
628	**188**	10d turquoise, green				
		and blue	40	25	☐	☐
	Set of 3	.. ..	60	40	☐	☐
	First Day Cover	.. ..		2·50		☐

189 Hammer Beam Roof, Westminster Hall

190 Palace of Westminster

Seventh Commonwealth Parliamentary Conference

1961 (25 Sept.)

629	**189**	6d purple and gold	20	20	☐	☐
630	**190**	1s 3d green and blue	2·50	2·00	☐	☐
	Set of 2	.. ..	2·60	2·10	☐	☐
	First Day Cover ..	..		24·00		☐

191 'Units of Productivity'

192 'National Productivity'

193 'Unified Productivity'

National Productivity Year

1962 (14 Nov.) *Wmk* **179** (*inverted on 2½d and 3d*)

631	**191**	2½d green and red ..	15	10	☐	☐
		p. Phosphor ..	50	40	☐	☐
632	**192**	3d blue and violet ..	15	10	☐	☐
		p. Phosphor ..	50	50	☐	☐
633	**193**	1s 3d red, blue and				
		green	2·25	1·60	☐	☐
		p. Phosphor ..	20·00	21·00	☐	☐
	Set of 3 (Ordinary)	.. ..	2·40	1·60	☐	☐
	Set of 3 (Phosphor)	.. ..	20·00	21·00	☐	☐
	First Day Cover (Ordinary) ..			24·00		☐
	First Day Cover (Phosphor)			80·00		☐

194 Campaign Emblem and Family

195 Children of Three Races

Freedom from Hunger

1963 (21 Mar.) *Wmk* **179** (*inverted*)

634	**194**	2½d crimson and pink	10	10	☐	☐
		p. Phosphor ..	1·00	1·00	☐	☐
635	**195**	1s 3d brown and yellow	2·50	2·50	☐	☐
		p. Phosphor ..	23·00	18·00	☐	☐
	Set of 2 (Ordinary)	.. ..	2·60	2·50	☐	☐
	Set of 2 (Phosphor)	.. ..	24·00	19·00	☐	☐
	First Day Cover (Ordinary) ..			24·00		☐
	First Day Cover (Phosphor)..			25·00		☐

196 'Paris Conference'

Paris Postal Conference Centenary

1963 (7 MAY) *Wmk* **179** (*inverted*)

636	**196**	6d green and mauve	40	40	☐	☐
		p. Phosphor	5·00	6·50	☐	☐
		First Day Cover (Ordinary) ..		12·00		☐
		First Day Cover (Phosphor) ..		22·00		☐

197 Posy of Flowers

198 Woodland Life

National Nature Week

1963 (16 MAY)

637	**197**	3d multicoloured ..	8	8	☐	☐
		p. Phosphor ..	50	50	☐	☐
638	**198**	4½d multicoloured ..	30	25	☐	☐
		p. Phosphor ..	3·50	3·00	☐	☐
		Set of 2 (Ordinary) ..	35	30	☐	☐
		Set of 2 (Phosphor) ..	4·00	3·50	☐	☐
		First Day Cover (Ordinary)		12·00		☐
		First Day Cover (Phosphor)		24·00		☐

199 Rescue at Sea

200 19th-century Lifeboat

201 Lifeboatmen

Ninth International Lifeboat Conference, Edinburgh

1963 (31 MAY)

639	**199**	2½d blue, black and red	10	10	☐	☐
		p. Phosphor ..	40	50	☐	☐
640	**200**	4d red, yellow, brown, black and blue	40	30	☐	☐
		p. Phosphor ..	20	50	☐	☐
641	**201**	1s 6d sepia, yellow and blue	4·50	4·00	☐	☐
		p. Phosphor ..	25·00	28·00	☐	☐
		Set of 3 (Ordinary)	4·50	4·00	☐	☐
		Set of 3 (Phosphor)	25·00	28·00	☐	☐
		First Day Cover (Ordinary)		25·00		☐
		First Day Cover (Phosphor)		28·00		☐

202 Red Cross

203

204

205 'Commonwealth Cable'

Red Cross Centenary Congress

1963 (15 AUG.)

642	**202**	3d red and lilac ..	10	10	☐	☐
		p. Phosphor ..	60	60	☐	☐
643	**203**	1s 3d red, blue and grey ..	2·50	3·25	☐	☐
		p. Phosphor ..	35·00	35·00	☐	☐
644	**204**	1s 6d red, blue and bistre ..	2·50	3·25	☐	☐
		p. Phosphor ..	20·00	20·00	☐	☐
		Set of 3 (Ordinary) ..	4·50	6·00	☐	☐
		Set of 3 (Phosphor) ..	50·00	50·00	☐	☐
		First Day Cover (Ordinary) ..		25·00		☐
		First Day Cover (Phosphor)		60·00		☐

Opening of COMPAC (Trans-Pacific Telephone Cable)

1963 (3 DEC.)

645	**205**	1s 6d blue and black	4·00	3·25	☐	☐
		p. Phosphor ..	20·00	20·00	☐	☐
		First Day Cover (Ordinary) ..		18·00		☐
		First Day Cover (Phosphor)		22·00		☐

206 Puck and Bottom
(*A Midsummer Night's Dream*)

207 Feste (*Twelfth Night*)

I. P. – 48

208 Balcony Scene
(*Romeo and Juliet*)

209 'Eve of Agincourt'
(*Henry V*)

I. 70

210 Hamlet contemplating Yorick's skull (*Hamlet*) and Queen Elizabeth II

Shakespeare Festival

1964 (23 APR.) *Perf* 11 × 12 (2s 6d) *or* 15 × 14 (*others*).

646	**206**	3d multicoloured ..	10	10	□	□
		p. *Phosphor* ..	20	20	□	□
647	**207**	6d multicoloured ..	20	20	□	□
		p. *Phosphor* ..	60	40	□	□
648	**208**	1s 3d multicoloured ..	1·00	1·25	□	□
		p. *Phosphor* ..	8·00	8·00	□	□
649	**209**	1s 6d multicoloured ..	1·25	1·25	□	□
		p. *Phosphor* ..	8·00	8·00	□	□
650	**210**	2s 6d deep slate-purple	2·00	2·00	□	□
		Set of 5 (*Ordinary*)	4·25	4·25	□	□
		Set of 4 (*Phosphor*) ..	15·00	14·00	□	□
		First Day Cover (*Ordinary*)		10·00		□
		First Day Cover (*Phosphor*)		14·00		□
		Presentation Pack (*Ordinary*)	6·00		□	

PRESENTATION PACKS were first introduced by the G.P.O. for the Shakespeare Festival issue. The packs include one set of stamps and details of the designs, the designer and the stamp printer. They were issued for almost all later definitive and special issues.

For note about Presentation Packs in foreign languages, see page 25.

211 Flats near Richmond Park
('Urban Development')

212 Shipbuilding Yards, Belfast
('Industrial Activity')

I - 50

I - 10

213 Beddgelert Forest Park, Snowdonia ('Forestry')

214 Nuclear Reactor, Dounreay ('Technological Development')

20th International Geographical Congress, London

1964 (1 JULY)

651	**211**	2½d multicoloured ..	10	10	□	□
		p. *Phosphor* ..	50	40	□	□
652	**212**	4d multicoloured ..	25	25	□	□
		p. *Phosphor* ..	90	70	□	□
653	**213**	8d multicoloured ..	50	50	□	□
		p. *Phosphor* ..	2·00	1·75	□	□
654	**214**	1s 6d multicoloured ..	4·00	3·75	□	□
		p. *Phosphor* ..	25·00	25·00	□	□
		Set of 4 (*Ordinary*) ..	4·50	4·25	□	□
		Set of 4 (*Phosphor*) ..	25·00	25·00	□	□
		First Day Cover (*Ordinary*) ..		18·00		□
		First Day Cover (*Phosphor*)		25·00		□
		Presentation Pack (*Ordinary*)	75·00		□	

215 Spring Gentian

216 Dog Rose

I - 30

I - 60

217 Honeysuckle

218 Fringed Water Lily

Tenth International Botanical Congress, Edinburgh

1964 (5 AUG.)

655	**215**	3d multicoloured ..	10	10	□	□
		p. *Phosphor* ..	20	20	□	□
656	**216**	6d multicoloured ..	20	20	□	□
		p. *Phosphor* ..	1·25	1·40	□	□
657	**217**	9d multicoloured ..	2·25	2·25	□	□
		p. *Phosphor* ..	3·75	5·00	□	□
658	**218**	1s 3d multicoloured ..	2·60	2·10	□	□
		p. *Phosphor* ..	26·00	26·00	□	□
		Set of 4 (*Ordinary*) ..	4·50	4·25	□	□
		Set of 4 (*Phosphor*) ..	26·00	26·00	□	□
		First Day Cover (*Ordinary*)		18·00		□
		First Day Cover (*Phosphor*)		28·00		□
		Presentation Pack (*Ordinary*)	75·00		□	

I-1/I.P-20

219 Forth Road Bridge

220 Forth Road and Railway Bridges

Opening of Forth Road Bridge

1964 (4 Sept.)

659	**219**	3d black, blue and violet	8	8	☐	☐
		p. Phosphor	40	50	☐	☐
660	**220**	6d black, blue and red	35	40	☐	☐
		p. Phosphor	4·00	5·50	☐	☐
	Set of 2 (Ordinary)		40	45	☐	☐
	Set of 2 (Phosphor)		4·00	6·00	☐	☐
	First Day Cover (Ordinary)			5·00		☐
	First Day Cover (Phosphor)			7·00		☐
	Presentation Pack (Ordinary)		£180			☐

221 Sir Winston Churchill

I - 1

222 Sir Winston Churchill

I - 15

Churchill Commemoration

1965 (8 July)

661	**221**	4d black and drab	8	8	☐	☐
		p. Phosphor	30	30	☐	☐
662	**222**	1s 3d black and grey	35	30	☐	☐
		p. Phosphor	4·00	3·50	☐	☐
	Set of 2 (Ordinary)		40	35	☐	☐
	Set of 2 (Phosphor)		4·25	3·75	☐	☐
	First Day Cover (Ordinary)			2·00		☐
	First Day Cover (Phosphor)			4·50		☐
	Presentation Pack (Ordinary)		10·00			☐

223 Simon de Montfort's Seal

I - 5

224 Parliament Buildings (after engraving by Hollar, 1647)

700th Anniversary of Simon de Montfort's Parliament

1965 (19 July)

663	**223**	6d green	10	10	☐	☐
		p. Phosphor	40	40	☐	☐
664	**224**	2s 6d black, grey and drab	1·25	1·25	☐	☐
	Set of 2 (Ordinary)		1·25	1·25	☐	☐
	First Day Cover (Ordinary)			10·00		☐
	First Day Cover (Phosphor)			9·00		☐
	Presentation Pack (Ordinary)		26·00		☐	

225 Bandsmen and Banner

226 Three Salvationists

Salvation Army Centenary

1965 (9 Aug.)

665	**225**	3d multicoloured	10	10	☐	☐
		p. Phosphor	40	40	☐	☐
666	**226**	1s 6d multicoloured	1·00	1·00	☐	☐
		p. Phosphor	4·00	4·25	☐	☐
	Set of 2 (Ordinary)		1·10	1·10	☐	☐
	Set of 2 (Phosphor)		4·25	4·25	☐	☐
	First Day Cover (Ordinary)			16·00		☐
	First Day Cover (Phosphor)			18·00		☐

I - 4D

227 Lister's Carbolic Spray

228 Lister and Chemical Symbols

Centenary of Joseph Lister's Discovery of Antiseptic Surgery

1965 (1 Sept.)

667	**227**	4d indigo, chestnut and grey	10	10	☐	☐
		p. Phosphor	15	20	☐	☐
668	**228**	1s black, purple and blue	1·00	1·25	☐	☐
		p. Phosphor	1·60	1·60	☐	☐
	Set of 2 (Ordinary)		1·10	1·25	☐	☐
	Set of 2 (Phosphor)		1·75	1·75	☐	☐
	First Day Cover (Ordinary)			7·00		☐
	First Day Cover (Phosphor)			7·00		☐

229 Trinidad Carnival Dancers   **230** Canadian Folk-dancers

Commonwealth Arts Festival
1965 (1 SEPT.)

669	**229**	6d black and orange	10	10	□	□
		p. Phosphor	20	20	□	□
670	**230**	1s 6d black and violet	1·40	1·40	□	□
		p. Phosphor	1·40	1·40	□	□
		Set of 2 (Ordinary)	1·50	1·50	□	□
		Set of 2 (Phosphor)	1·60	1·60	□	□
		First Day Cover (Ordinary)		8·00		□
		First Day Cover (Phosphor)		9·00		□

231 Flight of Spitfires   **232** Pilot in Hurricane

233 Wing-tips of Spitfire and Messerschmitt 'ME-109'   **234** Spitfires attacking Heinkel 'HE-111' Bomber

235 Spitfire attacking Stuka Dive-bomber   **236** Hurricanes over Wreck of Dornier 'DO-17z2' Bomber

The above were issued together *se-tenant* in blocks of six (3 × 2) within the sheet.

I - 10   I - 6

237 Anti-aircraft Artillery in Action   **238** Air-battle over St Paul's Cathedral

25th Anniversary of Battle of Britain
1965 (13 SEPT.)

671	**231**	4d olive and black	30	35	□	□
	a.	Block of 6				
		Nos. 671/6	5·00	5·00	□	□
	p.	Phosphor	40	50	□	□
	pa.	Block of 6				
		Nos. 671p/6p	6·00	8·00	□	□
672	**232**	4d olive, blackish olive and black	30	35	□	□
	p.	Phosphor	40	50	□	□
673	**233**	4d multicoloured	30	35	□	□
	p.	Phosphor	40	50	□	□
674	**234**	4d olive and black	30	35	□	□
	p.	Phosphor	40	50	□	□
675	**235**	4d olive and black	30	35	□	□
	p.	Phosphor	40	50	□	□
676	**236**	4d multicoloured	30	35	□	□
	p.	Phosphor	40	50	□	□
677	**237**	9d black, violet, orange and maroon	1·25	1·25	□	□
	p.	Phosphor	80	80	□	□
678	**238**	1s 3d green, black and blue	1·25	1·25	□	□
	p.	Phosphor	80	80	□	□
		Set of 8 (Ordinary)	6·50	4·25	□	□
		Set of 8 (Phosphor)	7·50	4·25	□	□
		First Day Cover (Ordinary)		12·00		□
		First Day Cover (Phosphor)		15·00		□
		Presentation Pack (Ordinary)	42·00		□	

I - 17 / I.P - 20

239 Tower and Georgian Buildings   **240** Tower and 'Nash' Terrace, Regent's Park

Opening of Post Office Tower
1965 (8 OCT.)

679	**239**	3d yellow, blue and green	10	10	□	□
	p.	Phosphor	5	8	□	□
680	**240**	1s 3d green and blue	40	45	□	□
	p.	Phosphor	30	40	□	□
		Set of 2 (Ordinary)	45	50	□	□
		Set of 2 (Phosphor)	35	45	□	□
		First Day Cover (Ordinary)		4·00		□
		First Day Cover (Phosphor)		5·00		□
		Presentation Pack (Ordinary)	1·25		□	
		Presentation Pack (Phosphor)	1·25		□	

241 U.N. Emblem **242** I.C.Y. Emblem

20th Anniversary of UNO and International Co-operation Year

1965 (25 Oct.)

681	**241**	3d	blk, orge & bl ..	15	10	☐	☐
		p.	Phosphor	15	10	☐	☐
682	**242**	1s 6d	blk, pur & bl ..	1·00	75	☐	☐
		p.	Phosphor	1·10	80	☐	☐
		Set of 2 (Ordinary)	.. ..	1·10	85	☐	☐
		Set of 2 (Phosphor)	.. ..	1·25	90	☐	☐
		First Day Cover (Ordinary) ..		8·00		☐	
		First Day Cover (Phosphor)		7·00		☐	

I-3/I.P - 20

243 Telecommunications Network **244** Radio Waves and Switchboard

I.T.U. Centenary

1965 (15 Nov.)

683	**243**	9d	multicoloured ..	20	20	☐	☐
		p.	Phosphor	60	50	☐	☐
684	**244**	1s 6d	multicoloured ..	1·40	1·10	☐	☐
		p.	Phosphor	4·50	6·00	☐	☐
		Set of 2 (Ordinary)	.. ..	1·50	1·25	☐	☐
		Set of 2 (Phosphor)	.. ..	5·00	6·50	☐	☐
		First Day Cover (Ordinary) ..		7·00		☐	
		First Day Cover (Phosphor)		9·00		☐	

245 Robert Burns (after Skirving chalk drawing) **246** Robert Burns (after Nasmyth portrait)

Burns Commemoration

1966 (25 Jan.)

685	**245**	4d	blk, indigo & bl ..	15	10	☐	☐
		p.	Phosphor ..	15	10	☐	☐
686	**246**	1s 3d	blk, bl & orge ..	70	55	☐	☐
		p.	Phosphor ..	85	70	☐	☐
		Set of 2 (Ordinary)	.. ..	85	60	☐	☐
		Set of 2 (Phosphor)	.. ..	1·00	80	☐	☐
		First Day Cover (Ordinary) ..		2·00		☐	
		First Day Cover (Phosphor)		2·50		☐	
		Presentation Pack (Ordinary)		16·00		☐	

247 Westminster Abbey **248** Fan Vaulting. Henry VII Chapel

900th Anniversary of Westminster Abbey

1966 (28 Feb.) *Perf 15 × 14 (3d) or 11 × 12 (2s 6d)*

687	**247**	3d	black, brown and blue ..	15	5	☐	☐
		p.	Phosphor ..	15	20	☐	☐
688	**248**	2s 6d	black ..	70	75	☐	☐
		Set of 2		85	75	☐	☐
		First Day Cover (Ordinary) ..		4·00			☐
		First Day Cover (Phosphor)		6·00			☐
		Presentation Pack (Ordinary)	12·00		☐	

I-1/I.P - 12

249 View near Hassocks, Sussex **250** Antrim, Northern Ireland

I-3/I.P -

251 Harlech Castle, Wales **252** Cairngorm Mountains, Scotland

Landscapes

1966 (2 May)

689	**249**	4d	black, yellow-green and blue	15	8	☐	☐
		p.	Phosphor ..	15	8	☐	☐
690	**250**	6d	black, green and blue	15	10	☐	☐
		p.	Phosphor ..	15	20	☐	☐
691	**251**	1s 3d	black, yellow and blue ..	35	30	☐	☐
		p.	Phosphor ..	35	30	☐	☐
692	**252**	1s 6d	black, orange and blue ..	50	45	☐	☐
		p.	Phosphor ..	50	45	☐	☐
		Set of 4 (Ordinary)	.. ..	1·00	80	☐	☐
		Set of 4 (Phosphor)	.. ..	1·00	80	☐	☐
		First Day Cover (Ordinary)		5·00			☐
		First Day Cover (Phosphor)		6·00			☐

4d

World Cup 1966 HARRISON AND SONS LTD.

253 Players with Ball

4d ENGLAND WINNERS

World Cup 1966 HARRISON AND SONS LTD.

260 Cup Winners

I - 25 / IP - 1

WORLD CUP 1966 WILLIAM KEMPSTER HARRISON AND SONS LTD. 6d

254 Goalmouth Mêlée

WORLD CUP 1966 DAVID CAPLAN HARRISON AND SONS LTD. 1/3

255 Goalkeeper saving Goal

World Cup Football Competition

1966 (1 June)

693	**253**	4d multicoloured ..		15	10	☐	☐
		p. Phosphor	..	15	10	☐	☐
694	**254**	6d multicoloured ..		20	20	☐	☐
		p. Phosphor	..	20	10	☐	☐
695	**255**	1s 3d multicoloured ..		50	35	☐	☐
		p. Phosphor	..	50	35	☐	☐
		Set of 3 (Ordinary)	..	75	55	☐	☐
		Set of 3 (Phosphor)	..	75	50	☐	☐
		First Day Cover (Ordinary) ..			5·00		☐
		First Day Cover (Phosphor)			5·00		☐
		Presentation Pack (Ordinary)	7·50			☐	

I - 4 / I.P. - 25   »

BLACK-HEADED GULL J NORRIS WOOD HARRISON AND SONS LTD. 4d

256 Black-headed Gull

BLUE TIT J NORRIS WOOD HARRISON AND SONS LTD. 4d

257 Blue Tit

ROBIN J NORRIS WOOD HARRISON AND SONS LTD. 4d

258 Robin

BLACKBIRD J NORRIS WOOD HARRISON AND SONS LTD. 4d

259 Blackbird

The above were issued se-tenant in blocks of four within the sheet.

British Birds

1966 (8 Aug.)

696	**256**	4d multicoloured ..		10	15	☐	☐
		a. Block of 4					
		Nos. 696/9		90	90	☐	☐
		p. Phosphor	..	10	15	☐	☐
		pa. Block of 4					
		Nos. 696p/9p ..		90	90	☐	☐
697	**257**	4d multicoloured ..		10	15	☐	☐
		p. Phosphor	..	10	15	☐	☐
698	**258**	4d multicoloured ..		10	15	☐	☐
		p. Phosphor	..	10	15	☐	☐
699	**259**	4d multicoloured ..		10	15	☐	☐
		p. Phosphor	..	10	15	☐	☐
		Set of 4 (Ordinary)	..	90	50	☐	☐
		Set of 4 (Phosphor)	..	90	50	☐	☐
		First Day Cover (Ordinary) ..			6·00		☐
		First Day Cover (Phosphor)			5·00		☐
		Presentation Pack (Ordinary)	3·50			☐	

England's World Cup Football Victory

1966 (18 Aug.)

700	**260**	4d multicoloured ..		20	10	☐	☐
		First Day Cover	.. ..		1·00		☐

4d D GILLESPIE HARRISON AND SONS LTD.

261 Jodrell Bank Radio Telescope

6d D GILLESPIE HARRISON AND SONS LTD.

262 British Motor-cars

SR N6 Hovercraft 1/3 A ANDREW RESTALL HARRISON AND SONS LTD.

263 SR N6 Hovercraft

Nuclear power Advanced gas-cooled reactor Windscale A ANDREW RESTALL HARRISON AND SONS LTD. 1/6

264 Windscale Reactor

British Technology

1966 (19 Sept.)

701	**261**	4d black and lemon		15	8	☐	☐
		p. Phosphor	..	15	8	☐	☐
702	**262**	6d red, blue and					
		orange	.. ..	15	12	☐	☐
		p. Phosphor	..	15	15	☐	☐
703	**263**	1s 3d multicoloured ..		30	30	☐	☐
		p. Phosphor	..	35	30	☐	☐
704	**264**	1s 6d multicoloured ..		40	30	☐	☐
		p. Phosphor	..	45	40	☐	☐
		Set of 4 (Ordinary)	.. ..	90	70	☐	☐
		Set of 4 (Phosphor)	.. ..	1·00	85	☐	☐
		First Day Cover (Ordinary) ..			2·00		☐
		First Day Cover (Phosphor)			2·40		☐
		Presentation Pack (Ordinary)	4·00			☐	

I-5 / I.P-4

265 **266**

267 **268**

269 **270**

The above show battle scenes, they were issued together
se-tenant in horizontal strips of six within the sheet.

I-15 / I.P.-15

271 Norman Ship

I-12 / I.P.-3

272 Norman Horsemen attacking Harold's Troops

900th Anniversary of Battle of Hastings

1966 (14 OCT.) *Designs show scenes from Bayeux Tapestry.*
Wmk **179** *(sideways on 1s 3d)*

705	265	4d multicoloured ..		10	15	☐	☐
	a.	Strip of 6					
		Nos. 705/10 ..		1·50	2·00	☐	☐
	p.	Phosphor ..		10	25	☐	☐
	pa.	Strip of 6					
		Nos. 705p/10p		1·50	2·00	☐	☐
706	266	4d multicoloured ..		10	15	☐	☐
	p.	Phosphor ..		10	25	☐	☐
707	267	4d multicoloured ..		10	15	☐	☐
	p.	Phosphor ..		10	25	☐	☐
708	268	4d multicoloured ..		10	15	☐	☐
	p.	Phosphor ..		10	25	☐	☐
709	269	4d multicoloured ..		10	15	☐	☐
	p.	Phosphor ..		10	25	☐	☐
710	270	4d multicoloured ..		10	15	☐	☐
	p.	Phosphor ..		10	25	☐	☐
711	271	6d multicoloured ..		10	10	☐	☐
	p.	Phosphor ..		10	10	☐	☐
712	272	1s 3d multicoloured ..		20	20	☐	☐
	p.	Phosphor ..		20	20	☐	☐
		Set of 8 (Ordinary) ..		1·60	1·10	☐	☐
		Set of 8 (Phosphor) ..		1·60	1·60	☐	☐
		First Day Cover (Ordinary)			2·50		☐
		First Day Cover (Phosphor)			2·50		☐
		Presentation Pack (Ordinary)		3·25			☐

273 King of the Orient

I-2 / IP-15

274 Snowman

Christmas

1966 (1 DEC.) Wmk **179** *(upright on 1s 6d)*

713	273	3d multicoloured ..	5	5	☐	☐
	p.	Phosphor ..	5	5	☐	☐
714	274	1s 6d multicoloured ..	35	25	☐	☐
	p.	Phosphor ..	35	25	☐	☐
		Set of 2 (Ordinary)	40	30	☐	☐
		Set of 2 (Phosphor) ..	40	30	☐	☐
		First Day Cover (Ordinary)		1·00		☐
		First Day Cover (Phosphor)		1·00		☐
		Presentation Pack (Ordinary)	3·00			☐

I-8 / I.P.-3   *IP-8*

275 Sea Freight

276 Air Freight

European Free Trade Association (EFTA)

1967 (20 FEB.)

715	275	9d multicoloured ..	15	10	☐	☐
	p.	Phosphor ..	15	10	☐	☐
716	276	1s 6d multicoloured ..	30	20	☐	☐
	p.	Phosphor ..	30	20	☐	☐
		Set of 2 (Ordinary)	40	30	☐	☐
		Set of 2 (Phosphor) ..	40	30	☐	☐
		First Day Cover (Ordinary)		1·00		☐
		First Day Cover (Phosphor)		1·00		☐
		Presentation Pack (Ordinary)	1·25			☐

277 Hawthorn and Bramble

278 Larger Bindweed and Viper's Bugloss

279 Ox-eye Daisy, Coltsfoot and Buttercup

280 Bluebell, Red Campion and Wood Anemone

The above were issued together *se-tenant* in blocks of four within the sheet.

281 Dog Violet

282 Primroses

British Wild Flowers

1967 (24 APR.)

717	**277**	4d multicoloured ..	15	10	☐	☐
		a. *Block of 4*				
		Nos. 717/20 ..	1·00	95	☐	☐
		p. *Phosphor* ..	10	10	☐	☐
		pa. *Block of 4*				
		Nos. 717p/20p	70	55	☐	☐
718	**278**	4d multicoloured ..	15	10	☐	☐
		p. *Phosphor* ..	10	10	☐	☐
719	**279**	4d multicoloured ..	15	10	☐	☐
		p. *Phosphor* ..	10	10	☐	☐
720	**280**	4d multicoloured ..	15	10	☐	☐
		p. *Phosphor* ..	10	10	☐	☐
721	**281**	9d multicoloured ..	15	10	☐	☐
		p. *Phosphor* ..	10	10	☐	☐
722	**282**	1s 9d multicoloured ..	20	20	☐	☐
		p. *Phosphor* ..	20	20	☐	☐
		Set of 6 (Ordinary)	1·25	65	☐	☐
		Set of 6 (Phosphor) ..	90	65	☐	☐
		First Day Cover (Ordinary)		2·00		☐
		First Day Cover (Phosphor)		1·60		☐
		Presentation Pack (Ordinary)	2·00			☐

PRESENTATION PACKS IN FOREIGN LANGUAGES

German Presentation Packs are similar to the English versions but have the text printed in German. From the 1969 Collectors Pack until the end of 1974 they were replaced by separately printed insert cards in German. Similar cards in Japanese and Dutch were available from 1969 British Ships issue until end of 1974. A pack printed in Japanese was, however, issued for the 1972 Royal Silver Wedding set.

283 (value at left)

284 (value at right)

   I   II

Two types of the 2d.

I. Value spaced away from left side of stamp.

II. Value close to left side from new multi-positive. This results in the portrait appearing in the centre, thus conforming with the other values.

1967–69 *Two phosphor bands, except where otherwise stated. No wmk*

723	**283**	½d orange-brown	5	20	☐	☐	40
724		1d olive (2 bands)	8	10	☐	☐	
725		1d olive (1 centre band)	25	30	☐	☐	
726		2d lake-brown (Type I) (2 bands)	10	12	☐	☐	12
727		2d lake-brown (Type II) (2 bands)	15	15	☐	☐	
728		2d lake-brown (Type II) (1 centre band) ..	40	50	☐	☐	
729		3d violet (1 centre band)	10	10	☐	☐	
730		3d violet (2 bands)	30	30	☐	☐	
731		4d sepia (2 bands)	8	10	☐	☐	
732		4d olive-brown (1 centre band) ..	10	10	☐	☐	
733		4d vermilion (1 centre band) ..	8	10	☐	☐	
734		4d vermilion (1 side band) ..	1·40	1·60	☐	☐	
735		5d blue	10	10	☐	☐	
736		6d purple	20	20	☐	☐	2·5
737	**284**	7d emerald ..	40	30	☐	☐	30
738		8d vermilion ..	12	30	☐	☐	3·00
739		8d turquoise-blue	45	50	☐	☐	60
740		9d green	50	30	☐	☐	19
741	**283**	10d drab ..	45	50	☐	☐	30
742		1s violet	40	30	☐	☐	40
743		1s 6d blue & dp blue ..	50	30	☐	☐	8
		b. *Phosphorised paper*	75	90	☐	☐	
744		1s 9d orange & black	40	30	☐	☐	35
		Set of 16 (one of each value and colour)	3·00	3·25	☐	☐	
		Presentation Pack (one of each value)	6·00			☐	
		Presentation Pack (German)	40·00			☐	

No. 734 exists with the phosphor band at the left or right. For prices of First Day Covers and for listing of decimal issue, Nos. X841/X1019, see pages 32/6.

285 'Master Lambton'
(Sir Thomas Lawrence)

P/O -5

286 'Mares and Foals in a
Landscape' (George Stubbs)

P/O - 400

287 'Children Coming Out
of School' (L. S. Lowry)

P/O - 200

288 Gipsy Moth IV

British Paintings

1967 (10 JULY) *Two phosphor bands. No wmk*

748	**285**	4d multicoloured	..	5	8	□	□
749	**286**	9d multicoloured	..	20	12	□	□
750	**287**	1s 6d multicoloured	..	35	20	□	□
	Set of 3	..	.. ..	50	35	□	□
	First Day Cover ..	..	..		1·10		□
	Presentation Pack	..	..	3·00		□	

Sir Francis Chichester's World Voyage

1967 (24 JULY) *Three phosphor bands. No wmk*

751	**288**	1s 9d multicoloured	..	15	15	□	□
	First Day Cover	..	..		50		□

I-8

289 Radar Screen

P/O - 1·50

290 Penicillin Mould

P/O - 6

I-10

291 'VC-10' Jet Engines

P/O - 400

292 Television Equipment

P/O-200

British Discovery and Invention

1967 (19 SEPT.) *Two phosphor bands (except 4d, three bands). Wmk* **179** *(sideways on 1s 9d)*

752	**289**	4d multicoloured	..	5	8	□	□
753	**290**	1s multicoloured	..	8	10	□	□
754	**291**	1s 6d multicoloured	..	25	15	□	□
755	**292**	1s 9d multicoloured	..	30	20	□	□
	Set of 4	..	.. ..	60	45	□	□
	First Day Cover	..	..		80		□
	Presentation Pack	..	..	1·50		□	

NO WATERMARK. All the following issues are on un watermarked paper unless stated.

P/o - c

293 'The Adoration of
the Shepherds'
(School of Seville)

P/O - 8

294 'Madonna and
Child' (Murillo)

P/O - 9

295 'The Adoration of the Shepher
(Louis Le Nain)

Christmas

1967 *Two phosphor bands (except 3d, one phosphor band*

756	**293**	3d multicoloured (27 Nov.)	..	5	5	□	
757	**294**	4d multicoloured (18 Oct.)	..	10	5	□	
758	**295**	1s 6d multicoloured (27 Nov.)	..	30	20	□	
	Set of 3	..	.. ..	40	25	□	
	First Day Covers (2)	..	..		1·00		

Gift Pack 1967

1967 (27 Nov.) *Comprises Nos. 715p/22p and 748/58*

	Gift Pack	..	..	..	2·50	□

1967–68 *No wmk Perf 11×12*

759	**166**	2s 6d brown	..	..	40	45	□	
760	**167**	5s red ..	..	..	1·00	1·00	□	
761	**168**	10s blue	..	..	5·00	5·50	□	
762	**169**	£1 black	..	..	3·00	4·00	□	
	Set of 4	..	.. ..		8·50	10·00	□	

26

296 Tarr Steps, Exmoor
P/O - 8

297 Aberfeldy Bridge
P/O - 11

298 Menai Bridge
P/O - 27

299 M4 Viaduct
P/O - 6

British Bridges

1968 (29 APR.) *Two phosphor bands*

763	**296**	4d multicoloured ..	5	5	□	□
764	**297**	9d multicoloured ..	8	10	□	□
765	**298**	1s 6d multicoloured ..	20	15	□	□
766	**299**	1s 9d multicoloured ..	25	20	□	□
		Set of 4	50	45	□	□
		First Day Cover		1·10	□	
		Presentation Pack	1·25		□	

300 'TUC' and Trades Unionists
P/O - 7

301 Mrs Emmeline Pankhurst (statue)
P/O - 5

302 Sopwith 'Camel' and 'Lightning' Fighters
P/O - 6

303 Captain Cook's *Endeavour* and Signature
P/O - 120

British Anniversaries. Events described on stamps

1968 (29 MAY) *Two phosphor bands*

767	**300**	4d green, olive, blue and black ..	5	5	□	□
768	**301**	9d violet, grey and black ..	8	12	□	□
769	**302**	1s multicoloured ..	20	15	□	□
770	**303**	1s 9d ochre and brown	25	20	□	□
		Set of 4	50	45	□	□
		First Day Cover		3·25	□	
		Presentation Pack	1·60		□	

304 'Queen Elizabeth I' (Unknown Artist)
P/O - 8

305 'Pinkie' (Lawrence)
P/O - 4

306 'Ruins of St Mary Le Port' (Piper)
P/O - 4

307 'The Hay Wain' (Constable)
P/O - 12

British Paintings

1968 (12 AUG.) *Two phosphor bands*

771	**304**	4d multicoloured ..	5	5	□	□
772	**305**	1s multicoloured ..	15	15	□	□
773	**306**	1s 6d multicoloured ..	20	15	□	□
774	**307**	1s 9d multicoloured ..	25	20	□	□
		Set of 4	60	50	□	□
		First Day Cover		1·00	□	
		Presentation Pack	1·40		□	
		Presentation Pack (German)	6·00		□	

Gift Pack 1968

1968 (16 SEPT.) *Comprises Nos.* 763/74

Gift Pack	7·00	□
Gift Pack (German)	18·00	□

Collectors Pack 1968

1968 (16 SEPT.) *Comprises Nos.* 752/8 *and* 763/74

Collectors Pack	6·00	□

308 Girl and Boy with Rocking Horse

309 Girl with Doll's House   **310** Boy with Train Set

Christmas

1968 (25 Nov.) *Two phosphor bands (except 4d, one centre phosphor band)*

775	**308**	4d multicoloured ..	5	5	☐	☐
776	**309**	9d multicoloured ..	15	12	☐	☐
777	**310**	1s 6d multicoloured ..	25	15	☐	☐
		Set of 3	40	25	☐	☐
		First Day Cover		60		☐
		Presentation Pack	1·40		☐	
		Presentation Pack (German)	6·00		☐	

311 RMS *Queen Elizabeth 2*

312 Elizabethan Galleon   **313** East Indiaman

P/O
– 35

314 *Cutty Sark*

315 SS *Great Britain*

The 9d and 1s values were arranged in horizontal strips of three and pairs respectively throughout the sheet.

P/O
– 40

316 RMS *Mauretania*

British Ships

1969 (15 Jan.) *Two phosphor bands (except 5d, one horiz phosphor band, 1s, two vert phosphor bands at right)*

778	**311**	5d multicoloured ..	5	5	☐	☐
779	**312**	9d multicoloured ..	10	15	☐	☐
		a. Strip of 3				
		Nos. 779/81	85	85		
780	**313**	9d multicoloured ..	10	15	☐	☐
781	**314**	9d multicoloured ..	10	15	☐	☐
782	**315**	1s multicoloured ..	25	25	☐	☐
		a. Pair. Nos. 782/3	90	85		
783	**316**	1s multicoloured ..	25	25	☐	☐
		Set of 6	1·60	90		
		First Day Cover		3·25		☐
		Presentation Pack	2·50		☐	
		Presentation Pack (German)	22·00		☐	

P/
–

317 'Concorde' in Flight   **318** Plan and Elevation Views

319 'Concorde's' Nose and Tail   **320** (See also Type **359a**)

First Flight of 'Concorde'

1969 (3 Mar.) *Two phosphor bands*

784	**317**	4d multicoloured ..	8	8	☐	☐
785	**318**	9d multicoloured ..	20	20	☐	☐
786	**319**	1s 6d deep blue, grey and light blue ..	30	20	☐	☐
		Set of 3	50	40	☐	☐
		First Day Cover		80		☐
		Presentation Pack	2·00		☐	
		Presentation Pack (German)	18·00		☐	

1969 (5 Mar.) *P 12*

787	**320**	2s 6d brown	50	30	☐	☐
788		5s lake	2·00	60	☐	☐
789		10s ultramarine ..	6·00	7·50	☐	☐
790		£1 black	3·00	1·60	☐	☐
		Set of 4	10·00	9·00	☐	☐
		Presentation Pack	18·00		☐	
		Presentation Pack (German)	45·00		☐	

321 Page from the *Daily Mail*, and Vickers 'Vimy' Aircraft

322 Europa and C.E.P.T. Emblems

323 I.L.O. Emblem

324 Flags of N.A.T.O. Countries

325 Vickers 'Vimy' Aircraft and Globe showing Flight

Anniversaries. Events described on stamps

1969 (2 APR.) *Two phosphor bands*

791	**321**	5d multicoloured ..	5	5	□	□
792	**322**	9d multicoloured ..	20	20	□	□
793	**323**	1s claret, red and blue ..	20	12	□	□
794	**324**	1s 6d multicoloured ..	20	15	□	□
795	**325**	1s 9d turquoise-green, yellow and sepia	25	20	□	□
	Set of 5		80	70	□	□
	First Day Cover			1·25	□	
	Presentation Pack		2·25		□	
	Presentation Pack (German)		40·00		□	

326 Durham Cathedral

327 York Minster

328 St Giles' Cathedral, Edinburgh

329 Canterbury Cathedral

The above were issued together *se-tenant* in blocks of four within the sheet.

330 St Paul's Cathedral

331 Liverpool Metropolitan Cathedral

British Architecture (Cathedrals)

1969 (28 MAY) *Two phosphor bands*

796	**326**	5d multicoloured ..	8	8	□	□
	a	*Block of* 4				
		Nos. 796/9	85	1·00	□	□
797	**327**	5d multicoloured ..	8	8	□	□
798	**328**	5d multicoloured ..	8	8	□	□
799	**329**	5d multicoloured ..	8	8	□	□
800	**330**	9d multicoloured ..	12	12	□	□
801	**331**	1s 6d multicoloured ..	15	15	□	□
	Set of 6		1·00	55	□	□
	First Day Cover			1·75	□	
	Presentation Pack		2·40		□	
	Presentation Pack (German)		22·00		□	

332 The King's Gate, Caernarvon Castle

333 The Eagle Tower, Caernarvon Castle

334 Queen Eleanor's Gate, Caernarvon Castle

335 Celtic Cross, Margam Abbey

The 5d values were printed *se-tenant* in strips of three throughout the sheet.

336 Prince Charles

337 Mahatma Gandhi

P/o - 35

29

Investiture of H.R.H. The Prince of Wales

1969 (1 July) *Two phosphor bands*

802	**332**	5d multicoloured ..	5	10	□	□
		a. Strip of 3				
		Nos. 802/4 ..	60	75	□	□
803	**333**	5d multicoloured ..	5	10	□	□
804	**334**	5d multicoloured ..	5	10	□	□
805	**335**	9d multicoloured ..	10	10	□	□
806	**336**	1s black and gold	10	10	□	□
		Set of 5	70	45	□	□
		First Day Cover		1·00		□
		Presentation Pack ..	1·40			□
		Presentation Pack (German)	16·00			□

Gandhi Centenary Year

1969 (13 Aug.) *Two phosphor bands*

807	**337**	1s 6d black, green and				
		orange ..	20	20	□	□
		First Day Cover		50		□

Collectors Pack 1969

1969 (15 Sept.) *Comprises Nos. 775/86 and 791/807*

	Collectors Pack	22·00	□

338 National Giro

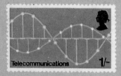

339 Telecommunications

340 Telecommunications

341 Automatic Sorting

P/0 - 300

British Post Office Technology

1969 (1 Oct.) *Two phosphor bands*   *Perf 13½ × 14*

808	**338**	5d multicoloured ..	10	5	□	□
809	**339**	9d multicoloured ..	15	10	□	□
810	**340**	1s multicoloured ..	15	15	□	□
811	**341**	1s 6d multicoloured ..	35	30	□	□
		Set of 4	70	55	□	□
		First Day Cover		90		□
		Presentation Pack ..	1·90			□

342 Herald Angel

343 The Three Shepherds

344 The Three Kings

Christmas

1969 (26 Nov.) *Two phosphor bands (5d, 1s 6d) or one centre band (4d)*

812	**342**	4d multicoloured ..	10	8	□	□
813	**343**	5d multicoloured ..	10	8	□	□
814	**344**	1s 6d multicoloured ..	30	25	□	□
		Set of 3	45	35	□	□
		First Day Cover		50		□
		Presentation Pack ..	1·90			□

345 Fife Harling

346 Cotswold Limestone

347 Welsh Stucco

348 Ulster Thatch

British Rural Architecture

1970 (11 Feb.) *Two phosphor bands*

815	**345**	5d multicoloured ..	10	5	□	□
816	**346**	9d multicoloured ..	20	20	□	□
817	**347**	1s multicoloured ..	20	20	□	□
818	**348**	1s 6d multicoloured ..	35	20	□	□
		Set of 4	75	60	□	□
		First Day Cover		1·00		□
		Presentation Pack	1·90			□

349 Signing the Declaration of Arbroath

350 Florence Nightingale attending Patients

P/0 -125

351 Signing of International Co-operative Alliance

352 Pilgrims and *Mayflower*

353 Sir William Herschel, Francis Baily, Sir John Herschel and Telescope

358 'Grasmere' (from engraving by J. Farrington, R.A.)

Literary Anniversaries. *Events described on stamps*

1970 (3 JUNE) *Two phosphor bands*

824	**354**	5d multicoloured ..	8	10	☐	☐
		a. *Block of 4*				
		Nos. 824/7 ..	90	90	☐	☐
825	**355**	5d multicoloured ..	8	10	☐	☐
826	**356**	5d multicoloured ..	8	10	☐	☐
827	**357**	5d multicoloured ..	8	10	☐	☐
828	**358**	1s 6d multicoloured ..	20	20	☐	☐
		Set of 5	1·00	55	☐	☐
		First Day Cover		1·50		☐
		Presentation Pack ..	2·25			☐

Anniversaries. *Events described on stamps*

1970 (1 APR.) *Two phosphor bands*

819	**349**	5d multicoloured ..	10	5	☐	☐
820	**350**	9d multicoloured ..	15	12	☐	☐
821	**351**	1s multicoloured ..	15	12	☐	☐
822	**352**	1s 6d multicoloured ..	30	20	☐	☐
823	**353**	1s 9d multicoloured ..	30	25	☐	☐
		Set of 5	90	65	☐	☐
		First Day Cover		1·25		☐
		Presentation Pack	2·25			☐

359   **359a** (Value redrawn)

Decimal Currency

1970 (17 JUNE)–**72** *10p and some printings of the 50p were issued on phosphor paper   Perf 12*

829	**359**	10p cerise ..	75	75	☐	☐
830		20p olive-green ..	60	15	☐	☐
831		50p ultramarine ..	1·40	40	☐	☐
831*b*	**359a**	£1 black ..	2·75	75	☐	☐
		Set of 4	5·75	1·75	☐	☐
829/31		*Presentation Pack* ..	7·00			☐
790 (or 831*b*), 830/1						
		Presentation Pack	8·00			☐

For First Day Cover prices see pages 35/6.

354 'Mr Pickwick and Sam' (*Pickwick Papers*)

355 'Mr and Mrs Micawber' (*David Copperfield*)

360 Runners P⟨O ~ 150

361 Swimmers P⟨O – 65

356 'David Copperfield and Betsy Trotwood' (*David Copperfield*)

357 'Oliver asking for more' (*Oliver Twist*)

362 Cyclists

The 5d values were issued together *se-tenant* in blocks of four within the sheet.

Ninth British Commonwealth Games

1970 (15 JULY) *Two phosphor bands* *Perf* $13\frac{1}{2} \times 14$

832	**360**	5d	pink, emerald, greenish yellow & yellow-green	8	8	☐	☐
833	**361**	1s 6d	greenish blue, lilac, brown and Prussian blue ..	40	35	☐	☐
834	**362**	1s 9d	yellow-orange, lilac, salmon and red-brown	40	35	☐	☐
	Set of 3	.. ..		80	70	☐	☐
	First Day Cover				80		☐
	Presentation Pack			2·00			☐

Collectors Pack 1970

1970 (14 SEPT.) *Comprises Nos. 808/28 and 832/4*

	Collectors Pack	.. .. ..	26·00			☐

363 1d Black
(1840)

364 1s Green
(1847)

365 4d Carmine
(1855)

'Philympia 70' Stamp Exhibition

1970 (18 SEPT.) *Two phosphor bands* *Perf* $14 \times 14\frac{1}{2}$

835	**363**	5d	multicoloured ..	10	5	☐	☐
836	**364**	9d	multicoloured ..	35	30	☐	☐
837	**365**	1s 6d	multicoloured ..	40	30	☐	☐
	Set of 3	.. ..		75	60	☐	☐
	First Day Cover				1·00		☐
	Presentation Pack			1·90			☐

366 Shepherds and
Apparition of the Angel

367 Mary, Joseph, and
Christ in the Manger

P/O - 3

368 The Wise Men
bearing Gifts

Christmas

1970 (25 NOV.) *Two phosphor bands* (5d, 1s 6d) *or one centre phosphor band* (4d)

838	**366**	4d multicoloured ..		5	5	☐	☐
839	**367**	5d multicoloured ..		5	5	☐	☐
840	**368**	1s 6d multicoloured ..		45	25	☐	☐
	Set of 3	.. ..		50	30	☐	☐
	First Day Cover				60		☐
	Presentation Pack			2·00			☐

369

369a

Decimal Currency

1971–89. *Type* **369**

(a) *Printed in photogravure by Harrison and Sons with phosphor bands. Perf* 15×14

X841	$\frac{1}{2}$p turq-bl (2 bands) ..		5	5	☐	☐
X842	$\frac{1}{2}$p turq-bl (1 side band) ..	65·00	32·00		☐	☐
X843	$\frac{1}{2}$p turquoise-blue (1 centre band)		20	20	☐	☐
X844	1p crimson (2 bands) ..		5	5	☐	☐
X845	1p crim (1 centre band) ..		12	12	☐	☐
X846	1p crimson ('all-over' phosphor)		10	20	☐	☐
X847	1p crimson (1 side band)		40	45	☐	☐
X848	$1\frac{1}{2}$p black (2 bands)		10	15	☐	☐
X849	2p myr-grn (face value as in T **369**) (2 bands)		8	5	☐	☐
X850	2p myr-grn (face value as in T **369**) 'all-over' phosphor		10	15	☐	☐
X851	$2\frac{1}{2}$p mag (1 centre band) ..		10	10	☐	☐
X852	$2\frac{1}{2}$p magenta (1 side band)	1·40	1·60		☐	☐
X853	$2\frac{1}{2}$p magenta (2 bands) ..		20	30	☐	☐
X854	$2\frac{1}{2}$p rose-red (2 bands) ..		25	30	☐	☐
X855	3p ultramarine (2 bands) ..		20	10	☐	☐
X856	3p ultram (1 centre band) ..		12	25	☐	☐
X857	3p bright magenta (2 bands)		20	25	☐	☐
X858	$3\frac{1}{2}$p olive-grey (2 bands) ..		30	30	☐	☐
X859	$3\frac{1}{2}$p ol-grey (1 centre band)		20	15	☐	☐

P/O - 50   P/O - 1·50

X860	3½p purple-brown (1 centre band) ..	1·25	1·00	□ □	
X861	4p ochre-brown (2 bands)	15	15	□ □	*35*
X862	4p greenish bl (2 bands)	2·00	1·75	□ □	
X863	4p greenish blue (1 centre band) ..	45	60	□ □	*85*
X864	4p greenish blue (1 side band)	1·00	1·10	□ □	
X865	4½p grey-blue (2 bands) ..	20	25	□ □	
X866	5p pale violet (2 bands) ..	20	10	□ □	*300*
X867	5p claret (1 centre band)	40	75	□ □	
X868	5½p violet (2 bands)	25	25	□ □	
X869	5½p violet (1 centre band)	20	20	□ □	
X870	6p light emerald (2 bands)	20	12	□ □	*300*
X871	6½p greenish bl (2 bands)	35	45	□ □	
X872	6½p greenish blue (1 centre band) ..	20	15	□ □	
X873	6½p greenish blue (1 side band)	35	55	□ □	
X874	7p purple-brn (2 bands)	25	15	□ □	
X875	7p purple-brown (1 centre band) ..	20	10	□ □	
X876	7p purple-brown (1 side band)	30	30	□ □	
X877	7½p chestnut (2 bands)	30	25	□ □	*100*
X878	8p rosine (2 bands) ..	25	20	□ □	*150*
X879	8p rosine (1 centre band)	25	15	□ □	
X880	8p rosine (1 side band) ..	40	45	□ □	
X881	8½p yellowish green (2 bands) ..	25	12	□ □	
X882	9p yellow-orange and black (2 bands) ..	45	30	□ □	*55*
X883	9p deep violet (2 bands)	30	20	□ □	
X884	9½p purple (2 bands)	35	30	□ □	*12*
X885	10p orange-brown and chestnut (2 bands) ..	40	30	□ □	
X886	10p orange-brn (2 bands)	30	8	□ □	
X887	10p orange-brown ('all-over' phosphor) ..	30	45	□ □	
X888	10p orange-brown (1 centre band) ..	30	20	□ □	
X889	10p orange-brown (1 side band)	40	60	□ □	
X890	10½p yellow (2 bands)	30	30	□ □	
X891	10½p blue (2 bands) ..	40	45	□ □	
X892	11p brown-red (2 bands)	30	25	□ □	
X893	11½p drab (1 centre band) ..	35	30	□ □	
X894	11½p drab (1 side band)	40	45	□ □	
X895	12p yellowish green (2 bands)	35	40	□ □	
X896	12p bright emerald (1 centre band)	20	25	□ □	
X897	12p bright emerald (1 side band)	35	55	□ □	
X898	12½p light emerald (1 centre band)	35	25	□ □	
X899	12½p light emerald (1 side band)	40	45	□ □	
X900	13p pale chestnut (1 centre band) ..	20	25	□ □	
X901	13p pale chestnut (1 side band) ..	35	45	□ □	
X902	14p grey-blue (2 bands) ..	50	45	□ □	*23*

X903	14p dp bl (1 centre band)	25	30	□ □	
X904	14p dp blue (1 side band)	25	30	□ □	
X904q	15p brt bl (1 centre band)	25	30	□ □	
X904r	15p brt blue (1 side band)	25	30	□ □	
X905	15½p pale violet (2 bands)	45	45	□ □	
X906	16p olive-drab (2 bands) ..	1·50	1·75	□ □	*30*
X907	17p grey-blue (2 bands) ..	50	55	□ □	
X908	18p dp ol-grey (2 bands)	50	60	□ □	*100*
X909	19p bright orange-red (2 bands) ..	30	35	□ □	*125*
X910	20p dull purple (2 bands)	60	25	□ □	
X910a	20p brownish black (2 bands) ..	30	30	□ □	
X911	26p rosine (2 bands)	2·50	2·25	□ □	
X912	31p purple (2 bands) .	2·50	2·75	□ □	*650*
X913	34p ochre-brown (2 bands)	2·50	2·75	□ □	*750*
X914	50p ochre-brown (2 bands)	1·40	30	□ □	

(b) Printed in photogravure by Harrison and Sons on phosphorised paper. Perf 15 × 14

X924	½p turquoise-blue ..	10	5	□ □	
X925	1p crimson	5	5	□ □	
X926	2p myrtle-green (face value as in T 369) ..	10	5	□ □	
X927	2p deep green (smaller value as in T 369a) ..	5	10	□ □	
X928	2p myr-grn (smaller value as in T 369a) ..	5	5	□ □	
X929	2½p rose-red	12	15	□ □	
X930	3p bright magenta ..	5	8	□ □	
X931	3½p purple-brown ..	35	30	□ □	
X932	4p greenish blue ..	15	20	□ □	
X933	4p new blue	8	10	□ □	
X934	5p pale violet ..	20	15	□ □	
X935	5p dull red-brown ..	8	10	□ □	
X936	7p red	1·50	1·00	□ □	
X937	8½p yellowish green ..	30	55	□ □	
X938	10p orange-brown ..	15	20	□ □	
X939	11p brown-red ..	60	75	□ □	
X940	11½p ochre-brown ..	50	45	□ □	
X941	12p yellowish green ..	35	30	□ □	
X942	13p olive-grey	50	45	□ □	
X943	13½p purple-brown ..	55	60	□ □	
X944	14p grey-blue ..	40	30	□ □	
X945	15p ultramarine ..	40	30	□ □	
X946	15½p pale violet ..	40	40	□ □	
X947	16p olive-drab ..	45	30	□ □	
X948	16½p pale chestnut ..	70	75	□ □	
X949	17p light emerald ..	60	40	□ □	
X950	17p grey-blue	45	25	□ □	
X951	17½p pale chestnut ..	60	60	□ □	
X952	18p deep violet ..	60	75	□ □	
X953	18p deep olive-grey ..	30	40	□ □	
X954	19p bright orange-red ..	30	35	□ □	
X955	19½p olive-grey	2·50	1·50	□ □	
X956	20p dull purple ..	60	20	□ □	
X957	20p turquoise-green ..	30	35	□ □	
X957a	20p brownish black ..	30	30	□ □	
X958	20½p ultramarine ..	90	75	□ □	
X959	22p blue	60	30	□ □	
X960	22p bright green ..	35	45	□ □	
X961	23p brown-red ..	1·10	45	□ □	
X962	23p bright green ..	35	40	□ □	

X963	24p violet	40	45	☐ ☐
X963*a*	24p Indian red	40	45	☐ ☐
X964	25p purple	75	90	☐ ☐
X965	26p rosine	40	30	☐ ☐
X966	27p chestnut	45	50	☐ ☐
X967	28p deep violet	45	40	☐ ☐
X968	28p ochre	45	50	☐ ☐
X969	29p ochre-brown	2·50	1·25	☐ ☐
X969*a*	29p deep mauve	45	50	☐ ☐
X969*b*	30p deep olive-grey	45	50	☐ ☐
X970	31p purple	50	45	☐ ☐
X971	32p greenish blue	50	55	☐ ☐
X972	34p ochre-brown	55	45	☐ ☐
X972*a*	34p deep bluish grey	55	55	☐ ☐
X973	35p sepia	55	60	☐ ☐
X973*a*	37p rosine	60	65	☐ ☐

(c) Printed in photogravure by Harrison and Sons on ordinary paper. Perf 15 × 14

X974	50p ochre-brown	75	45	☐ ☐
X975	75p grey-black (smaller value as T **369***a*)	1·10	1·25	☐ ☐

(d) Printed in lithography by John Waddington. Perf 13½ × 14

X996	4p greenish blue (2 bands)	15	25	☐ ☐
X997	4p greenish blue (phosphorised paper)	12	15	☐ ☐
X998	20p dull purple (2 bands)	60	40	☐ ☐
X999	20p dull purple (phosphorised paper)	55	25	☐ ☐

(e) Printed in lithography by Questa. Perf 13½ × 14 (Nos X1000, X1003/4 and X1014) or 15 × 14 (others)

X1000	2p emerald-green (face value as in T **369**) (phosphorised paper)	15	15	☐ ☐
	a Perf 15 × 14	15	15	☐ ☐
X1001	2p bright grn and dp grn (smaller value as in T **369***a*) (phosphorised paper)	15	15	☐ ☐
X1002	4p greenish blue (phosphorised paper)	15	15	☐ ☐
X1003	5p light violet (phosphorised paper)	20	20	☐ ☐
X1004	5p claret (phosphorised paper)	15	20	☐ ☐
	a Perf 15 × 14	8	15	☐ ☐
X1005	13p pale chest (1 centre band)	50	50	☐ ☐
X1006	13p pale chest (1 side band)	50	50	☐ ☐
X1007	dp bl (1 centre band)	25	30	☐ ☐
X1008	18p deep olive-grey (phosphorised paper)	50	60	☐ ☐
X1009	18p dp ol-grey (2 bands)	1·10	1·50	☐ ☐
X1010	19p bright orange-red (phosphorised paper)	30	35	☐ ☐
X1011	20p dull purple (phosphorised paper)	50	45	☐ ☐
X1012	22p yell-grn (2 bands)	1·60	1·50	☐ ☐
X1013	34p ochre-brn (2 bands)	1·60	1·50	☐ ☐

X1014	75p black (face value as T **369**) (ordinary paper)	2·00	1·50	☐ ☐
	a Perf 15 × 14	2·00	1·50	☐ ☐
X1015	75p brownish grey and black (smaller value as T **369***a*) (ordinary paper)	2·00	1·25	☐ ☐

(f) Printed in lithography by Walsall. Perf 14

X1016	14p deep blue (1 side band)	25	30	☐ ☐
X1017	19p bright orange-red (2 bands)	30	35	☐ ☐
X1019	29p deep mauve (2 bands)	45	50	☐ ☐

Presentation Pack (contains ½p (X841), 1p (X844), 1½p (X848), 2p (X849), 2½p (X851), 3p (X855), 3½p (X858), 4p (X861), 5p (X866), 6p (X870), 7½p (X877), 9p (X882)) — 4·00 ☐

Presentation Pack ('Scandinavia 71') (*contents as above*) — 32·00 ☐

Presentation Pack (contains ½p (X841), 1p (X844), 1½p (X848), 2p (X849), 2½p (X851), 3p (X855 or X856), 3½p (X858 or X859), 4p (X861), 4½p (X865), 5p (X866), 5½p (X868 or X869), 6p (X870), 6½p (X871 or X872), 7p (X874), 7½p (X877), 8p (X878), 9p (X882), 10p (X885)) — 4·00 ☐

Presentation Pack (contains ½p (X841), 1p (X844), 1½p (X848), 2p (X849), 2½p (X851), 3p (X856), 6p (X866), 6½p (X872), 7p (X874 or X875), 7½p (X877), 8p (X878), 8½p (X881), 9p (X883), 9½p (X884), 10p (X886), 10½p (X890), 11p (X892), 20p (X910), 50p (X914)) — 5·00 ☐

Presentation Pack (contains 2½p (X929), 3p (X930), 4p (X996), 10½p (X891), 11½p (X893), 11½p (X940), 12p (X941), 13p (X942), 13½p (X943), 14p (X944), 15p (X945), 15½p (X946), 17p (X949), 17½p (X951), 18p (X952), 22p (X959), 25p (X964), 75p (X1014)) — 12·00 ☐

Presentation Pack (contains ½p (X924), 1p (X925), 2p (X1000), 3p (X930), 3½p (X931), 4p (X997), 5p (X1004), 10p (X888), 12½p (X898), 16p (X947), 16½p (X948), 17p (X950), 20p (X999), 20½p (X958), 23p (X961), 26p (X965), 28p (X967), 31p (X970), 50p (X974), 75p (X1014)) — 19·00 ☐

Presentation Pack (contains ½p (X924), 1p (X925), 2p (X1000a), 3p (X930), 4p (X997), 5p (X1004a), 10p (X938), 13p (X900), 16p (X947), 17p (X950), 18p (X953), 20p (X999), 22p (X960), 24p (X963), 26p (X965), 28p (X967), 31p (X970), 34p (X972), 50p (X974), 75p (X1014a)) .. .. 15·00 □

Presentation Pack (contains 1p (X925), 2p (X1000a), 3p (X930), 4p (X997), 5p (X1004a), 7p (X936), 10p (X938), 12p (X896), 13p (X900), 17p (X950), 18p (X953), 20p (X999), 22p (X960), 24p (X963), 26p (X965), 28p (X967), 31p (X970), 34p (X972), 50p (X974), 75p (X1014a)) .. .. 6·50 □

Presentation Pack (contains 14p (X903), 19p (X954), 20p (X957), 23p (X962), 27p (X966), 28p (X968), 32p (X971), 35p (X973) .. 3·50 □

Presentation Pack (contains 15p (X904q), 20p (X957a), 24p (X963a), 29p (X969a), 30p (X969b), 34p (X972a), 37p (X973a) 3·25 □

"X" NUMBERS. These are provisional only and may be amended in future editions.

PHOSPHOR BANDS. See notes on page 15.
Phosphor bands are applied to the stamps, after the design has been printed, by a separate cylinder. On issues with "all-over" phosphor the "band" covers the entire stamp. Parts of the stamp covered by phosphor bands, or the entire surface for "all-over" phosphor versions, appear matt.
Nos. X847, X852, X864, X873, X876, X880, X889, X894,

PHOSPHORISED PAPER. First introduced as an experiment for a limited printing of the 1s 6d value (No. 743b) in 1969 this paper has the phosphor, to activate the automatic sorting machinery, added to the paper coating before the stamps were printed. Issues on this paper have a completely shiny surface. Although not adopted after this first trial further experiments on the 8½p in 1976 led to this paper being used for new printings of current values.

QUEEN ELIZABETH II DEFINITIVE FIRST DAY COVERS

The British Post Office did not introduce special First Day of Issue postmarks for definitive issues until the first instalment of the Machin £sd series, issued 5 June 1967, although "First Day" treatment had been provided for some Regional stamps from 8 June 1964 onwards.

1952–1966

PRICES for First Day Covers listed below are for stamps, as indicated, used on illustrated envelopes and postmarked with operational cancellations.

5 Dec. 1952	1½d, 2½d (Nos. 517, 519) ..	6·00	□
6 July 1953	5d, 8d, 1s (Nos. 522, 525, 529)	25·00	□
31 Aug. 1953	½d, 1d, 2d (Nos. 515/16, 518)	20·00	□
2 Nov. 1953	4d, 1s 3d, 1s 6d (Nos. 521, 530/1)	50·00	□
18 Jan. 1954	3d, 6d, 7d (Nos. 520, 523/4)	30·00	□
8 Feb. 1954	9d, 10d, 11d (Nos. 526/8) ..	60·00	□
1 Sept. 1955	10s, £1 (Nos. 538/9) ..	£400	□
23 Sept. 1955	2s 6d, 5s (Nos. 536/7) ..	£175	□
19 Nov. 1957	½d, 1d, 1½d, 2d, 2½d, 3d (graphite lines) (Nos. 561/6)	60·00	□
9 Feb. 1959	4½d (No. 577)	45·00	□

1967–1989

PRICES for First Day Covers listed below are for stamps, as indicated, used on illustrated envelopes and postmarked with the special First Day of Issue handstamps. Other definitives issued during this period were not accepted for "First Day" treatment by the British Post Office.

£sd Issues

5 June 1967	4d, 1s, 1s 9d (Nos.731,742, 744)	1·40	□
8 Aug. 1967	3d, 9d, 1s 6d (Nos.729,740, 743)	1·40	□
5 Feb. 1968	½d, 1d, 2d, 6d (Nos. 723/4, 726, 736)	75	□
1 July 1968	5d, 7d, 8d, 10d (Nos. 735, 737/8, 741)	1·10	□
5 March 1969	2s 6d, 5s, 10s, £1 (Nos. 787/90)	15·00	□

Decimal Issues

17 June 1970	10p, 20p, 50p, (Nos. 829/31)	5·50	□
15 Feb. 1971	½p, 1p, 1½p, 2p, 2½p, 3p, 3½p, 4p, 5p, 6p, 7½p, 9p (Nos. X841, X844, X848/9, X851, X855, X858, X861, X866, X870, X877, X882) (Covers carry "POSTING DELAYED BY THE POST OFFICE STRIKE 1971" cachet)	2·75	□
11 Aug. 1971	10p (No. X885)	1·00	□

6 Dec. 1972	£1 (*No.* 831*b*)	7·00	☐
24 Oct. 1973	4½p, 5½p, 8p, (*Nos.* X865, X868, X878)	1·00	☐
4 Sept. 1974	6½p (*No.* X871)	1·40	☐
15 Jan. 1975	7p (*No.* X874)	75	☐
24 Sept. 1975	8½p (*No.* X881)	1·25	☐
25 Feb. 1976	9p, 9½p, 10p, 10½p, 11p, 20p (*Nos.* X883/4, X886, X890, X892, X910)	2·75	☐
2 Feb. 1977	50p (*No.* X914)	2·25	☐
2 Feb. 1977	£1, £2, £5 (*Nos.* 1026, 1027/8)	20·00	☐
26 April 1978	10½p (*No.* X891)	1·00	☐
15 Aug. 1979	11½p, 13p, 15p (*Nos.* X940, X942, X945)	2·00	☐
30 Jan. 1980	4p, 12p, 13½p, 17p, 17½p, 75p (*Nos.* X996, X941, X943, X949, X951, X1014)	4·50	☐
22 Oct. 1980	3p, 22p, (*Nos.* X930, X959)	1·00	☐
14 Jan. 1981	2½p, 11½p, 14p, 15½p, 18p, 25p (*Nos.* X929, X893, X944, X946, X952, X964)	2·25	☐
27 Jan. 1982	5p, 12½p, 16½p, 19½p, 26p, 29p (*Nos.* X1004, X898, X948, X955, X965, X969)	3·25	☐
30 March 1983	3½p, 16p, 17p, 20½p, 23p, 28p, 31p, (*Nos.* X931, X947, X950, X958, X961, X967, X970)	6·00	☐
3 Aug. 1983	£1·30 (*No.* 1026*b*)	9·00	☐
28 Aug. 1984	13p, 18p, 22p, 24p, 34p, (*Nos.* X900, X953, X960, X963, X972)	5·00	☐
28 Aug. 1984	£1·33 (*No.* 1026*c*)	7·50	☐
17 Sept. 1985	£1·41 (*No.* 1026*d*)	6·50	☐
29 Oct. 1985	7p, 12p (*No.* X936, X896)	2·00	☐
2 Sept. 1986	£1·50 (*No.* 1026*e*)	7·00	☐
15 Sept. 1987	£1·60 (*No.* 1026*f*)	7·00	☐
23 Aug. 1988	14p, 19p, 20p, 23p, 27p, 28p, 32p, 35p (*Nos.* X903, X954, X957, X962, X966, X968, X971, X973)	4·25	☐
22 Aug. 1989	(1st), (2nd) (*Nos.* 1445/6)	1·10	☐
26 Sept. 1989	15p, 20p, 24p, 29p, 30p, 34p, 37p (*Nos.* X904*q*, X957*a*, X963*a*, X969*a*/*b*, X972*a*, X973*a*)	3·75	☐

370 'A Mountain Road'
(T. P. Flanagan)

371 'Deer's Meadow'
(Tom Carr)

P/0 - 12

372 'Slieve na brock'
(Colin Middleton)

P/0 - 10

'Ulster '71' Paintings

1971 (16 JUNE) *Two phosphor bands*

881	**370**	3p multicoloured ..		10	10	☐	☐
882	**371**	7½p multicoloured ..		75	80	☐	☐
883	**372**	9p multicoloured ..		75	80	☐	☐
	Set of 3	.. ..		1·40	1·50	☐	☐
	First Day Cover	.. ..			1·75		☐
	Presentation Pack	.. ..		2·75		☐	

373 John Keats
(150th Death Anniv)

374 Thomas Gray
(Death Bicentenary)

P/0 - 25

375 Sir Walter Scott
(Birth Bicentenary)

Literary Anniversaries. *Events described above*

1971 (28 JULY) *Two phosphor bands*

884	**373**	3p multicoloured ..		10	10	☐	☐
885	**374**	5p multicoloured ..		75	80	☐	☐
886	**375**	7½p multicoloured ..		75	80	☐	☐
	Set of 3	.. ..		1·40	1·50	☐	☐
	First Day Cover	.. ..			1·60		☐
	Presentation Pack	.. ..		2·40		☐	

376 Servicemen and Nurse
of 1921

377 Roman Centurion

P/0 - 400

378 Rugby Football, 1871

British Anniversaries. *Events described on stamps*

1971 (25 AUG.) *Two phosphor bands*

887	**376**	3p multicoloured ..		10	10	☐	☐
888	**377**	7½p multicoloured ..		90	90	☐	☐
889	**378**	9p multicoloured ..		1·00	1·00	☐	☐
	Set of 3	.. .. ..		1·75	1·75	☐	☐
	First Day Cover	.. ..			2·00		☐
	Presentation Pack	.. ..		3·00		☐	

379 Physical Sciences Building,
University College of
Wales, Aberystwyth

380 Faraday Building,
Southampton
University

381 Engineering Department,
Leicester University

382 Hexagon Restaurant,
Essex University

British Architecture (Modern University Buildings)

1971 (22 Sept.) *Two phosphor bands*

890	**379**	3p multicoloured	10	10	☐	☐
891	**380**	5p multicoloured	20	25	☐	☐
892	**381**	7½p multicoloured	80	80	☐	☐
893	**382**	9p multicoloured	1·60	1·60	☐	☐
		Set of 4	2·50	2·50	☐	☐
		First Day Cover		2·50		☐
		Presentation Pack	3·50		☐	

Collectors Pack 1971

1971 (29 Sept.) *Comprises Nos. 835/40 and 881/93*

Collectors Pack	32·00	☐

383 'Dream of the Wise Men'

384 'Adoration of the Magi'

385 'Ride of the Magi'

Christmas

1971 (13 Oct.) *Two phosphor bands (3p, 7½p) or one centre phosphor band (2½p)*

894	**383**	2½p multicoloured	8	8	☐	☐
895	**384**	3p multicoloured	10	10	☐	☐
896	**385**	7½p multicoloured	90	1·00	☐	☐
		Set of 3	1·00	1·10	☐	☐
		First Day Cover		2·00		☐
		Presentation Pack	3·25		☐	

386 Sir James Clark Ross

387 Sir Martin Frobisher

388 Henry Hudson   **389** Capt. Robert F. Scott

P/O - 175

British Polar Explorers

1972 (16 Feb.) *Two phosphor bands*

897	**386**	3p multicoloured	8	8	☐	☐
898	**387**	5p multicoloured	20	20	☐	☐
899	**388**	7½p multicoloured	65	65	☐	☐
900	**389**	9p multicoloured	1·10	1·10	☐	☐
		Set of 4	1·75	1·75	☐	☐
		First Day Cover		2·00		☐
		Presentation Pack	3·25		☐	

390 Statuette of Tutankhamun   **391** 19th-century Coastguard

P/O - 200

392 Ralph Vaughan Williams and Score

P/O - 20

Anniversaries. Events described on stamps

1972 (26 Apr.) *Two phosphor bands*

901	**390**	3p multicoloured	8	8	☐	☐
902	**391**	7½p multicoloured	70	80	☐	☐
903	**392**	9p multicoloured	70	65	☐	☐
		Set of 3	1·25	1·40	☐	☐
		First Day Cover		1·90		☐
		Presentation Pack	3·25		☐	

393 St Andrew's, Greensted-
juxta-Ongar, Essex

394 All Saints, Earls
Barton, Northants

395 St Andrew's,
Letheringsett, Norfolk

396 St Andrew's,
Helpringham, Lincs

397 St Mary the Virgin, Huish
Episcopi, Sornerset

British Architecture (Village Churches)

1972 (21 June) *Two phosphor bands*

904	**393**	3p multicoloured ..	8	8	☐	☐
905	**394**	4p multicoloured ..	20	20	☐	☐
906	**395**	5p multicoloured ..	20	25	☐	☐
907	**396**	7½p multicoloured ..	1·40	1·50	☐	☐
908	**397**	9p multicoloured ..	1·60	1·75	☐	☐
		Set of 5	3·25	3·50	☐	☐
		First Day Cover		3·75	☐	
		Presentation Pack	5·00		☐	

'Belgica '72' Souvenir Pack

1972 (24 June) *Comprises Nos. 894/6 and 904/8*

	Souvenir Pack	15·00	☐

398 Microphones, 1924–69

399 Horn Loudspeaker

400 TV Camera, 1972

401 Oscillator and Spark
Transmitter, 1897

Broadcasting Anniversaries. Events described on stamps

1972 (13 Sept.) *Two phosphor bands*

909	**398**	3p multicoloured ..	8	8	☐	☐
910	**399**	5p multicoloured ..	15	20	☐	☐
911	**400**	7½p multicoloured ..	1·00	1·00	☐	☐
912	**401**	9p multicoloured ..	1·00	1·00	☐	☐
		Set of 4	2·00	2·00	☐	☐
		First Day Cover		2·00		☐
		Presentation Pack	3·25		☐	

402 Angel holding Trumpet

403 Angel playing Lute

404 Angel playing Harp

Christmas

1972 (18 Oct.) *Two phosphor bands (3p, 7½p) or one centre phosphor band (2½p)*

913	402	2½p multicoloured ..	8	8	☐	☐
914	403	3p multicoloured ..	8	8	☐	☐
915	404	7½p multicoloured ..	70	50	☐	☐
		Set of 3	75	60	☐	☐
		First Day Cover		1·40	☐	
		Presentation Pack	2·00		☐	

405 Queen Elizabeth II and Prince Philip

406 'Europe'

Royal Silver Wedding

1972 (20 Nov.) *3p 'all-over' phosphor, 20p without phosphor*

916	405	3p slate-purple, indigo-blue and silver	10	10	☐	☐
917		20p slate-purple, reddish violet and silver ..	70	75	☐	☐
		Set of 2	75	80	☐	☐
		First Day Cover		1·25	☐	
		Presentation Pack	2·00		☐	
		Presentation Pack (Japanese)	4·00		☐	
		Souvenir Book	3·00		☐	
		Gutter Pair (3p)	90		☐	
		Traffic Light Gutter Pair (3p)	22·00		☐	

Collectors Pack 1972

1972 (20 Nov.) *Comprises Nos. 897/917*

	Collectors Pack	35·00	☐

Britain's Entry into European Communities

1973 (3 Jan.) *Two phosphor bands*

919	406	3p multicoloured ..	10	10	☐	☐
920		5p multicoloured (blue jigsaw) ..	25	35	☐	☐
		a. Pair. Nos. 920/1	1·50	1·60	☐	☐
921		5p multicoloured (green jigsaw)	25	35	☐	☐
		Set of 3	1·50	70	☐	☐
		First Day Cover		1·60	☐	
		Presentation Pack	2·50		☐	

Nos. 920/1 were issued horizontally *se-tenant* throughout the sheet.

407 Oak Tree

British Trees (1st issue)

1973 (28 Feb.) *Two phosphor bands*

922	407	9p multicoloured ..	50	45	☐	☐
		First Day Cover		70		☐
		Presentation Pack ..	2·50		☐	

See also No. 949.

408 David Livingstone

409 H. M. Stanley

The above were issued horizontally *se-tenant* throughout the sheet.

410 Sir Francis Drake

411 Sir Walter Raleigh

412 Charles Sturt

British Explorers

1973 (18 APR.) *'All-over' phosphor*

923	**408**	3p multicoloured ..	25	20	☐	☐
		a. *Pair. Nos. 923/4*	1·60	1·90	☐	☐
924	**409**	3p multicoloured ..	25	20	☐	☐
925	**410**	5p multicoloured ..	30	30	☐	☐
926	**411** ◂	7½p multicoloured ..	35	30	☐	☐
927	**412**	9p multicoloured ..	40	40	☐	☐
		Set of 5	2·50	1·25	☐	☐
		First Day Cover		2·50	☐	
		Presentation Pack	4·00		☐	

P/O
−65

413   **414**

415

County Cricket 1873–1973

1973 (16 MAY) *Designs show sketches of W. G. Grace by Harry Furniss. Queen's head in gold. 'All-over' phosphor*

928	**413**	3p black and brown	8	8	☐	☐
929	**414**	7½p black and green	1·25	1·40	☐	☐
930	**415**	9p black and blue	1·40	1·40	☐	☐
		Set of 3	2·40	2·50	☐	☐
		First Day Cover		2·50	☐	
		Presentation Pack	3·50		☐	
		Souvenir Book ..	7·50		☐	
		PHQ Card (No. 928)	50·00	£140	☐	☐

For full information on all future British issues, collectors should write to the British Post Office Philatelic Bureau, 20 Brandon Street, Edinburgh EH3 5TT

416 'Self-portrait' (Sir Joshua Reynolds)   **417** 'Self-portrait' (Sir Henry Raeburn)

418 'Nelly O'Brien' (Sir Joshua Reynolds)   **419** 'Rev R. Walker (The Skater)' (Sir Henry Raeburn)

Artistic Anniversaries. Events described on stamps

1973 (4 JULY) *'All-over' phosphor*

931	**416**	3p multicoloured ..	8	8	☐	☐
932	**417**	5p multicoloured ..	20	25	☐	☐
933	**418**	7½p multicoloured ..	70	70	☐	☐
934	**419**	9p multicoloured ..	90	90	☐	☐
		Set of 4	1·60	1·75	☐	☐
		First Day Cover		1·90		☐
		Presentation Pack	2·40		☐	

420 Court Masque Costumes   **421** St Paul's Church, Covent Garden

P/
−2

422 Prince's Lodging, Newmarket   **423** Court Masque Stage Scene

P/
−

400th Anniversary of the Birth of Inigo Jones

1973 (15 Aug.) *'All-over' phosphor*

935	**420**	3p black, gold and reddish lilac ..	10	15	☐	☐
		a. *Pair. Nos.* 935/6	35	40	☐	☐
936	**421**	3p black, gold and deep brown ..	10	15	☐	☐
937	**422**	5p black, gold and blue ..	40	45	☐	☐
		a. *Pair. Nos.* 937/8	2·40	2·40	☐	☐
938	**423**	5p black, gold and grey-olive ..	40	45	☐	☐
		Set of 4	2·50	1·10	☐	☐
		First Day Cover ..		2·50		☐
		Presentation Pack	2·75		☐	
		PHQ Card (No. 936) ..	£140	70·00	☐	☐

The 3p and 5p values were printed horizontally *se-tenant* within the sheet.

424 Palace of Westminster seen from Whitehall

425 Palace of Westminster seen from Millbank

19th Commonwealth Parliamentary Conference

1973 (12 Sept.) *'All-over' phosphor*

939	**424**	8p black, grey and pale buff ..	30	30	☐	☐
940	**425**	10p black and gold	40	40	☐	☐
		Set of 2	65	70	☐	☐
		First Day Cover ..		1·25		☐
		Presentation Pack	2·00		☐	
		Souvenir Book ..	8·00		☐	
		PHQ Card (No. 939) ..	48·00	90·00	☐	☐

P/O - 50

426 Princess Anne and Captain Mark Phillips

Royal Wedding

1973 (14 Nov.) *'All-over' phosphor*

941	**426**	3½p violet and silver	10	10	☐	☐
942		20p brown and silver	90	90	☐	☐
		Set of 2	1·00	1·00	☐	☐
		First Day Cover ..		1·25		☐
		Presentation Pack ..	2·00		☐	
		PHQ Card (No. 941) ..	10·00	22·00	☐	☐
		Set of 2 Gutter Pairs	6·00		☐	
		Set of 2 Traffic Light Gutter Pairs ..	£140		☐	

427

428

429

430

431

432 'Good King Wenceslas, the Page and Peasant'

The 3p values depict the carol 'Good King Wenceslas' and were printed horizontally *se-tenant* within the sheet.

Christmas

1973 (28 Nov.) *One phosphor band (3p) or 'all-over' phosphor (3½p)*

943	**427**	3p multicoloured ..	15	15	☐	☐
		a. *Strip of 5. Nos.* 943/7 ..	3·00	2·75	☐	☐
944	**428**	3p multicoloured ..	15	15	☐	☐
945	**429**	3p multicoloured ..	15	15	☐	☐
946	**430**	3p multicoloured ..	15	15	☐	☐
947	**431**	3p multicoloured ..	15	15	☐	☐
948	**432**	3½p multicoloured ..	15	15	☐	☐
		Set of 6 ..	3·00	80	☐	☐
		First Day Cover ..		2·75		☐
		Presentation Pack ..	3·25		☐	

Collectors Pack 1973

1973 (28 Nov.) *Comprises Nos.* 919/48

	Collectors Pack ..	28·00		☐

433 Horse Chestnut

43

British Trees (2nd issue)

1974 (27 Feb.) 'All-over' phosphor

949	**433**	10p multicoloured ..	50	50	☐	☐
		First Day Cover		1·00		☐
		Presentation Pack	2·25		☐	
		PHQ Card	£140	70·00	☐	☐
		Gutter Pair	3·00		☐	
		Traffic Light Gutter Pair	50·00		☐	

434 First Motor Fire-engine, 1904

435 Prize-winning Fire-engine, 1863

436 Steam Fire-engine, 1830

437 Fire-engine, 1766

200th Anniversary of Public Fire Services

1974 (24 Apr.) 'All-over' phosphor

950	**434**	3½p multicoloured ..	8	8	☐	☐
951	**435**	5½p multicoloured ..	25	25	☐	☐
952	**436**	8p multicoloured ..	60	65	☐	☐
953	**437**	10p multicoloured ..	80	85	☐	☐
		Set of 4	1·50	1·60	☐	☐
		First Day Cover		3·00		☐
		Presentation Pack ..	2·00		☐	
		PHQ Card (No. 950) ..	£140	60·00	☐	☐
		Set of 4 Gutter Pairs ..	4·00		☐	
		Set of 4 Traffic Light				
		Gutter Pairs	50·00		☐	

438 P & O Packet Peninsular, 1888

439 Farman Biplane, 1911

440 Airmail-blue Van and Postbox, 1930

441 Imperial Airways 'C' Class Flying-boat, 1937

Centenary of Universal Postal Union

1974 (12 June) 'All-over' phosphor

954	**438**	3½p multicoloured ..	8	8	☐	☐
955	**439**	5½p multicoloured ..	20	25	☐	☐
956	**440**	8p multicoloured ..	30	35	☐	☐
957	**441**	10p multicoloured ..	50	40	☐	☐
		Set of 4	1·00	1·00	☐	☐
		First Day Cover		1·40		☐
		Presentation Pack ..	2·00		☐	
		Set of 4 Gutter Pairs ..	4·00		☐	
		Set of 4 Traffic Light				
		Gutter Pairs	40·00		☐	

442 Robert the Bruce

443 Owain Glyndŵr

444 Henry the Fifth

445 The Black Prince

Medieval Warriors

1974 (10 July) 'All-over' phosphor

958	**442**	4½p multicoloured ..	10	10	☐	☐
959	**443**	5½p multicoloured ..	20	25	☐	☐
960	**444**	8p multicoloured ..	85	90	☐	☐
961	**445**	10p multicoloured ..	85	90	☐	☐
		Set of 4	1·90	1·90	☐	☐
		First Day Cover		2·50		☐
		Presentation Pack ..	3·50		☐	
		PHQ Cards (set of 4) ..	36·00	26·00	☐	☐
		Set of 4 Gutter Pairs ..	6·00		☐	
		Set of 4 Traffic Light				
		Gutter Pairs	50·00		☐	

446 Churchill in Royal Yacht Squadron Uniform

447 Prime Minister, 1940

448 Secretary for War and Air. 1919

449 War Correspondent, South Africa, 1899

Birth Centenary of Sir Winston Churchill

1974 (9 OCT.) Queen's head and inscription in silver. 'All-over' phosphor

962	**446**	4½p green and blue	12	12	□	□
963	**447**	5½p grey and black	20	25	□	□
964	**448**	8p rose and lake ..	45	40	□	□
965	**449**	10p stone and brown	45	45	□	□
		Set of 4	1·10	1·10	□	□
		First Day Cover		1·60	□	
		Presentation Pack.. ..	1·50		□	
		Souvenir Book	2·50		□	
		PHQ Card (No. 963) ..	8·00	12·00	□	□
		Set of 4 Gutter Pairs ..	4·00		□	
		Set of 4 Traffic Light Gutter Pairs	40·00		□	

450 'Adoration of the Magi' (York Minster, c. 1355)

451 'The Nativity' (St Helen's Church, Norwich, c. 1480)

452 'Virgin and Child' (Ottery St Mary Church, c. 1350)

453 'Virgin and Child' (Worcester Cathedral, c. 1224)

Christmas

1974 (27 Nov.) Designs show church roof bosses. One phosphor band (3½p) or 'all-over' phosphor (others)

966	**450**	3½p multicoloured ..	8	8	□	□
967	**451**	4½p multicoloured ..	10	10	□	□
968	**452**	8p multicoloured ..	35	35	□	□
969	**453**	10p multicoloured ..	35	35	□	□
		Set of 4	80	80	□	□
		First Day Cover		1·40	□	
		Presentation Pack ..	1·50		□	
		Set of 4 Gutter Pairs ..	4·00		□	
		Set of 4 Traffic Light Gutter Pairs	50·00		□	

1974 (27 Nov.) Comprises Nos 949/69

Collectors Pack	10·00		□

454 Invalid in Wheelchair

Health and Handicap Funds

1975 (22 JAN.) 'All-over' phosphor

970	**454**	4½p + 1½p blue and azure	10	12	□	□
		First Day Cover ..		65	□	
		Gutter Pair	30		□	
		Traffic Light Gutter Pair	80		□	

455 'Peace – Burial at Sea'

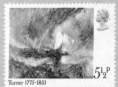

456 'Snowstorm – Steamer off a Harbour's Mouth'

457 'The Arsenal, Venice'

458 'St Laurent'

Birth Bicentenary of J. M. W. Turner

1975 (19 FEB.) 'All-over' phosphor

971	**455**	4½p multicoloured .	10	10	□	□
972	**456**	5½p multicoloured .	15	15	□	□
973	**457**	8p multicoloured .	20	25	□	□
974	**458**	10p multicoloured .	30	35	□	□
		Set of 4	70	80	□	□
		First Day Cover		1·25	□	
		Presentation Pack ..	1·50		□	
		PHQ Card (No. 972) ..	30·00	11·00	□	□
		Set of 4 Gutter Pairs ..	1·60		□	
		Set of 4 Traffic Light Gutter Pairs	6·00		□	

459 Charlotte Square,
Edinburgh

460 The Rows, Chester

The above were printed horizontally *se-tenant* throughout the sheet.

461 Royal Observatory,
Greenwich

462 St George's
Chapel, Windsor

463 National Theatre, London

European Architectural Heritage Year

1975 (23 APR.) 'All-over' phosphor

975	**459**	7p multicoloured ..		20	20	☐	☐
		a. Pair. Nos. 975/6		60	70	☐	☐
976	**460**	7p multicoloured ..		20	20	☐	☐
977	**461**	8p multicoloured ..		20	25	☐	☐
978	**462**	10p multicoloured ..		25	25	☐	☐
979	**463**	12p multicoloured ..		30	35	☐	☐
	Set of 5	.. ..		1·10	1·10	☐	☐
	First Day Cover	.. ..			1·75	☐
	Presentation Pack	.. ..		2·00		☐
	PHQ Cards (Nos. 975/7)			8·00	10·00	☐	☐
	Set of 5 Gutter Pairs	..		4·00		☐
	Set of 5 Traffic Light					
	Gutter Pairs	.. .. ..		15·00		☐

464 Sailing Dinghies

465 Racing Keel Boats

466 Cruising Yachts

467 Multihulls

P/O – 500

Sailing

1975 (11 JUNE) 'All-over' phosphor

980	**464**	7p multicoloured ..	20	20	☐	☐
981	**465**	8p multicoloured ..	20	20	☐	☐
982	**466**	10p multicoloured ..	25	25	☐	☐
983	**467**	12p multicoloured ..	35	45	☐	☐
	Set of 4	.. ..	90	1·00	☐	☐
	First Day Cover	.. ..		1·40	☐
	Presentation Pack ..	.. ..	1·25		☐
	PHQ Card (No. 981)	..	5·00	9·00	☐	☐
	Set of 4 Gutter Pairs	..	2·00		☐
	Set of 4 Traffic Light				
	Gutter Pairs	.. ..	20·00		☐

468 Stephenson's
Locomotion, 1825

469 Abbotsford,
1876

470 Caerphilly Castle, 1923

471 High Speed Train, 1975

150th Anniversary of Public Railways

1975 (13 AUG.) 'All-over' phosphor

984	**468**	7p multicoloured ..	30	35	☐	☐
985	**469**	8p multicoloured ..	30	40	☐	☐
986	**470**	10p multicoloured ..	40	45	☐	☐
987	**471**	12p multicoloured ..	50	60	☐	☐
	Set of 4	.. ..	1·40	1·60	☐	☐
	First Day Cover	.. ..		2·50	☐
	Presentation Pack	.. ..	2·25		☐
	Souvenir Book	.. ..	3·00		☐
	PHQ Cards (set of 4)	..	60·00	25·00	☐	☐
	Set of 4 Gutter Pairs	..	3·00		☐
	Set of 4 Traffic Light				
	Gutter Pairs	.. ..	12·00		☐

472 Palace of Westminster

62nd Inter-Parliamentary Union Conference

1975 (3 SEPT.) *'All-over' phosphor*

988	**472**	12p multicoloured ..	50	50	☐	☐
		First Day Cover		65		☐
		Presentation Pack	1·00		☐	
		Gutter Pair	1·00		☐	
		Traffic Light Gutter Pair ..	3·00		☐	

473 'Emma and Mr Woodhouse' (*Emma*)

474 'Catherine Morland' (*Northanger Abbey*)

475 'Mr Darcy' (*Pride and Prejudice*)

476 'Mary and Henry Crawford' (*Mansfield Park*)

Birth Bicentenary of Jane Austen (Novelist)

1975 (22 OCT.) *'All-over' phosphor*

989	**473**	8½p multicoloured ..	20	20	☐	☐
990	**474**	10p multicoloured ..	25	25	☐	☐
991	**475**	11p multicoloured ..	40	45	☐	☐
992	**476**	13p multicoloured ..	40	40	☐	☐
		Set of 4	1·10	1·10	☐	☐
		First Day Cover		1·40		☐
		Presentation Pack ..	2·00		☐	
		PHQ Cards (set of 4) ..	16·00	15·00	☐	☐
		Set of 4 Gutter Pairs ..	2·25		☐	
		Set of 4 Traffic Light Gutter Pairs	8·00		☐	

477 Angels with Harp and Lute

478 Angel with Mandolin

479 Angel with Horn

480 Angel with Trumpet

Christmas

1975 (26 NOV.) *One phosphor band* (6½p), *phosphor-inked* (8½p) *(background)* or *'all-over' phosphor (others)*

993	**477**	6½p multicoloured ..	20	15	☐	☐
994	**478**	8½p multicoloured ..	20	20	☐	☐
995	**479**	11p multicoloured ..	40	50	☐	☐
996	**480**	13p multicoloured ..	40	45	☐	☐
		Set of 4	1·10	1·10	☐	☐
		First Day Cover		1·25		☐
		Presentation Pack	2·00		☐	
		Set of 4 Gutter Pairs ..	2·25		☐	
		Set of 4 Traffic Light Gutter Pairs	8·00		☐	

Collectors Pack 1975

1975 (26 NOV.) *Comprises Nos.* 970/96

	Collectors Pack	8·00	☐

481 Housewife

482 Policeman

483 District Nurse

484 Industrialist

Telephone Centenary

1976 (10 Mar.) *'All-over' phosphor*

997	**481**	8½p multicoloured ..	20	20	☐	☐
998	**482**	10p multicoloured ..	25	25	☐	☐
999	**483**	11p multicoloured ..	40	45	☐	☐
1000	**484**	13p multicoloured ..	40	45	☐	☐
		Set of 4 ..	1·10	1·10	☐	☐
		First Day Cover		1·25		☐
		Presentation Pack	2·00		☐	
		Set of 4 Gutter Pairs	2·25		☐	
		Set of 4 Traffic Light Gutter Pairs	8·00		☐	

485 Hewing Coal (Thomas Hepburn) **486** Machinery (Robert Owen)

487 Chimney Cleaning (Lord Shaftesbury) **488** Hands clutching Prison Bars (Elizabeth Fry)

Social Reformers

1976 (28 Apr.) *'All-over phosphor*

1001	**485**	8½p multicoloured ..	20	20	☐	☐
1002	**486**	10p multicoloured ..	25	25	☐	☐
1003	**487**	11p black, slate and drab	40	45	☐	☐
1004	**488**	13p slate, black and green	40	45	☐	☐
		Set of 4	1·10	1·10	☐	☐
		First Day Cover		1·25		☐
		Presentation Pack	2·00		☐	
		PHQ Card (No. 1001) ..	6·00	7·00	☐	☐
		Set of 4 Gutter Pairs	2·25		☐	
		Set of 4 Traffic Light Gutter Pairs	8·00		☐	

489 Benjamin Franklin (bust by Jean-Jacques Caffieri)

Bicentenary of American Independence

1976 (2 June) *'All-over' phosphor*

1005	**489**	11p multicoloured ..	50	50	☐	☐
		First Day Cover		60		☐
		Presentation Pack	1·00		☐	
		PHQ Card	4·00	8·50	☐	☐
		Gutter Pair	1·00		☐	
		Traffic Light Gutter Pair ..	2·00		☐	

490 'Elizabeth of Glamis' **491** 'Grandpa Dickson'

492 'Rosa Mundi' **493** 'Sweet Briar'

Centenary of Royal National Rose Society

1976 (30 June) *'All-over' phosphor*

1006	**490**	8½p multicoloured ..	20	20	☐	☐
1007	**491**	10p multicoloured ..	30	30	☐	☐
1008	**492**	11p multicoloured ..	35	40	☐	☐
1009	**493**	13p multicoloured ..	35	35	☐	☐
		Set of 4	1·10	1·10	☐	☐
		First Day Cover		1·50		☐
		Presentation Pack	2·10		☐	
		PHQ Cards (set of 4) ..	30·00	14·00	☐	☐
		Set of 4 Gutter Pairs	2·40		☐	
		Set of 4 Traffic Light Gutter Pairs	10·00		☐	

494 Archdruid **495** Morris Dancing

P10 - £400

496 Scots Piper

497 Welsh Harpist

British Cultural Traditions

1976 (4 AUG.) *'All-over' phosphor*

1010	**494**	8½p multicoloured ..	20	20	□	□
1011	**495**	10p multicoloured ..	30	30	□	□
1012	**496**	11p multicoloured ..	35	35	□	□
1013	**497**	13p multicoloured ..	35	35	□	□
		Set of 4	1·10	1·10	□	□
		First Day Cover ..		1·25		□
		Presentation Pack ..	2·00		□	
		PHQ Cards (set of 4) ..	16·00	8·50	□	□
		Set of 4 Gutter Pairs ..	2·25		□	
		Set of 4 Traffic Light Gutter Pairs	8·00		□	

498 *The Canterbury Tales*

499 *The Tretyse of Love*

500 *Game and Playe of Chesse*   501 *Early Printing Press*

500th Anniversary of British Printing

1976 (29 SEPT.) *'All-over' phosphor*

1014	**498**	8½p blk, bl & gold ..	20	20	□	□
1015	**499**	10p blk, grn & gold ..	25	30	□	□
1016	**500**	11p blk, grey & gold ..	35	40	□	□
1017	**501**	13p brn, ochre & gold ..	40	45	□	□
		Set of 4	1·10	1·10	□	□
		First Day Cover		1·25		□
		Presentation Pack ..	2·10		□	
		PHQ Cards (set of 4) ..	13·00	8·50	□	□
		Set of 4 Gutter Pairs ..	2·25		□	
		Set of 4 Traffic Light Gutter Pairs	7·00		□	

502 Virgin and Child

503 Angel with Crown

504 Angel appearing to Shepherds

505 The Three Kings

Christmas

1976 (24 Nov.) *Designs show English mediaeval embroidery. One phosphor band (6½p) or 'all-over' phosphor (others)*

1018	**502**	6½p multicoloured ..	15	15	□	□
1019	**503**	8½p multicoloured ..	20	20	□	□
1020	**504**	11p multicoloured ..	35	40	□	□
1021	**505**	13p multicoloured ..	40	40	□	□
		Set of 4	1·00	1·10	□	□
		First Day Cover		1·25		□
		Presentation Pack ..	2·00		□	
		PHQ Cards (set of 4) ..	3·00	7·00	□	□
		Set of 4 Gutter Pairs ..	2·00		□	
		Set of 4 Traffic Light Gutter Pairs	7·00		□	

Collectors Pack 1976

1976 (24 Nov.) *Comprises Nos. 997/1021*

	Collectors Pack	12·00	□

506 Lawn Tennis

507 Table Tennis

508 Squash

509 Badminton

Racket Sports

1977 (12 JAN.) *Phosphorised paper*

1022	**506**	8½p multicoloured ..	20	20	☐	☐
1023	**507**	10p multicoloured ..	30	30	☐	☐
1024	**508**	11p multicoloured ..	35	40	☐	☐
1025	**509**	13p multicoloured ..	40	40	☐	☐
		Set of 4	1·10	1·10	☐	☐
		First Day Cover ..		1·50	☐	
		Presentation Pack ..	2·00		☐	
		PHQ Cards (set of 4)	6·00	8·50	☐	☐
		Set of 4 Gutter Pairs ..	2·25		☐	
		Set of 4 Traffic Light				
		Gutter Pairs	7·00		☐	

510

1977 (2 FEB.)–87 *Type* **510** *Ordinary paper*

1026	£1 green and olive	2·00	20	☐	☐
1026*b*	£1·30 drab & dp grnshd bl	8·00	6·00	☐	☐
1026*c*	£1·33 pale mve & grey-blk ..	6·50	3·75	☐	☐
1026*d*	£1·41 drab & dp grnshd bl	5·50	3·25	☐	☐
1026*e*	£1·50 pale mve & grey-blk ..	4·00	3·00	☐	☐
1026*f*	£1·60 drab and dp grnish bl	2·40	2·75	☐	☐
1027	£2 green and brown	4·00	75	☐	☐
1028	£5 pink and blue ..	10·00	3·50	☐	☐
	Presentation Pack (*Nos.* 1026, 1027/8)	15·00		☐	
	Presentation Pack (*No.* 1026*f*)	2·75		☐	

For First Day Cover prices see page 36.

511 Steroids – Conform-
ational Analysis

512 Vitamin C –
Synthesis

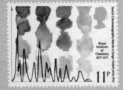

513 Starch –
Chromatography

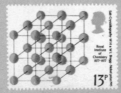

514 Salt –
Crystallography

Centenary of Royal Institute of Chemistry

1977 (2 MAR.) *'All-over' phosphor*

1029	**511**	8½p multicoloured ..	20	20	☐	☐
1030	**512**	10p multicoloured ..	30	30	☐	☐
1031	**513**	11p multicoloured ..	35	35	☐	☐
1032	**514**	13p multicoloured ..	40	40	☐	☐
		Set of 4 ..	1·10	1·10	☐	☐
		First Day Cover ..		1·40		☐
		Presentation Pack	2·40		☐	
		PHQ Cards (set of 4) ..	6·00	9·00	☐	☐
		Set of 4 Gutter Pairs ..	2·25		☐	
		Set of 4 Traffic Light				
		Gutter Pairs	7·00		☐	

515

516

517

518

(The designs differ in the decorations of 'ER'.)

Silver Jubilee

1977 (11 MAY–15 JUNE) *'All-over' phosphor*

1033	**515**	8½p multicoloured ..	20	20	☐	☐
1034		9p mult (15 June) ..	25	25	☐	☐
1035	**516**	10p multicoloured ..	25	30	☐	☐
1036	**517**	11p multicoloured ..	30	35	☐	☐
1037	**518**	13p multicoloured ..	40	40	☐	☐
		Set of 5	1·25	1·40	☐	☐
		First Day Covers (2)		1·75		☐
		Presentation Pack (ex 9p)	1·75		☐	
		Souvenir Book (ex 9p)	4·00		☐	
		PHQ Cards (set of 5)	12·00	8·00	☐	☐
		Set of 5 Gutter Pairs ..	2·75		☐	
		Set of 5 Traffic Light				
		Gutter Pairs	3·75		☐	

519 'Gathering of Nations'

Commonwealth Heads of Government Meeting, London

1977 (8 JUNE) *'All-over' phosphor*

1038	**519**	13p black, deep green rose and silver ..	50	50	☐	☐
		First Day Cover		90		☐
		Presentation Pack	1·00		☐	
		PHQ Card	3·00	3·75	☐	☐
		Gutter Pair	1·00		☐	
		Traffic Light Gutter Pair ..	1·25		☐	

520 Hedgehog

521 Brown Hare

522 Red Squirrel

523 Otter

T **520/4** were issued *se-tenant* throughout the sheet.

524 Badger

British Wildlife

1977 (5 OCT.) *'All-over' phosphor*

1039	**520**	9p multicoloured ..	25	20	☐	☐
		a. Strip of 5. Nos. 1039/43 ..	1·75	1·75	☐	☐
1040	**521**	9p multicoloured ..	25	20	☐	☐
1041	**522**	9p multicoloured ..	25	20	☐	☐
1042	**523**	9p multicoloured ..	25	20	☐	☐
1043	**524**	9p multicoloured ..	25	20	☐	☐
		Set of 5	1·75	90	☐	☐
		First Day Cover		2·00		☐
		Presentation Pack	2·10		☐	
		PHQ Cards (set of 5) ..	4·00	4·25	☐	☐
		Gutter Strip of 10 ..	3·75		☐	
		Traffic Light Gutter Strip of 10	4·00		☐	

525 'Three French Hens, Two Turtle Doves and a Partridge in a Pear Tree'

526 'Six Geese a-laying, Five Gold Rings, Four Colly Birds'

527 'Eight Maids a-milking, Seven Swans a-swimming'

528 'Ten Pipers piping, Nine Drummers drumming'

529 'Twelve Lords a-leaping, Eleven Ladies dancing'

530 'A Partridge in a Pear Tree'

T **525/30** depict the carol 'The Twelve Days of Christmas'. T **525/29** were printed horizontally *se-tenant* throughout the sheet.

Christmas

1977 (23 Nov.) *One centre phosphor band (7p) or 'all-over' phosphor (9p)*

1044	**525**	7p multicoloured ..	15	15	☐	☐
		a. Strip of 5 Nos. 1044/8 ..	1·00	1·10	☐	☐
1045	**526**	7p multicoloured ..	15	15	☐	☐
1046	**527**	7p multicoloured ..	15	15	☐	☐
1047	**528**	7p multicoloured ..	15	15	☐	☐
1048	**529**	7p multicoloured ..	15	15	☐	☐
1049	**530**	9p multicoloured ..	20	20	☐	☐
		Set of 6	1·10	85	☐	☐
		First Day Cover		1·40		☐
		Presentation Pack	2·00		☐	
		PHQ Cards (set of 6) ..	3·00	4·00	☐	☐
		Set of 6 Gutter Pairs ..	2·50		☐	
		Set of 6 Traffic Light Gutter Pairs	4·00		☐	

Collectors Pack 1977

1977 (23 Nov.) *Comprises Nos. 1022/5. 1029/49*

	Collectors Pack ..	7·00	☐

We can help you for all your Great Britain requirements . . . CONTACT RUSHSTAMPS!

COMPETITIVE PRICES, GOOD QUALITY & SPEEDY SERVICE! – FULLEST SATISFACTION OR REFUND (7 days)

Our latest RUSH EXPRESS 64-page price list is second to none in offering the full range of GB material from 1840 to date, including: Defs, Commems, Regionals, P. Dues, all as sets or singles, mint, used and space filler F.D.C.s, Pres. Packs, Booklets, Gutter Pairs, Errors & Varieties, Wartime Propaganda, Exhibition S/Shts, Special Collections and lots, Albums, Mounts, stock-books, etc. Br. Locals and Strike Mail, Cinderella, also Jersey, Guernsey and Isle of Man, and lots more!

Special exchange proposals, tempting offers and free gifts. Join the tens of thousands of collectors who order from us regularly (Annual Subscription is only £2, Overseas £5)

WE ARE MEMBERS of the Philatelic Traders Society (London) and the American Stamp Dealers Association (New York).

WE ALSO WISH TO BUY We require G.B. singles, sets, lots and Collections – send for offer or submit details – our GB Buying List is available on receipt of S.A.E. Worldwide Br. Comm. Collections also considered.

EXHIBITIONS We attend all major UK and International Exhibitions, come and see us at Stampex (London) in October 1989 and February 1990, ask for complimentary tickets (S.A.E. please).

£B1 FREE £1 DISCOUNT

WHICH CAN BE USED AGAINST ANY PURCHASE OVER £5 FROM THIS ADVERTISEMENT (see next page).

WE CATER FOR ALL CLASSES OF G.B. COLLECTORS – FROM BEGINNERS TO SPECIALISED.

MAY WE SERVE YOU!!

Rushstamps

(Retail) Ltd.

P.O. Box One, Lyndhurst
Hampshire SO43 7PP, England
Telephone: Lyndhurst (042128) 2044 (3 lines)
Fax: Lyndhurst (042128) 2981

20 very special offers to readers of 'COLLECT BRITISH STAMPS'

We guarantee delivery at these prices until the next edition of 'Collect British Stamps' is published in November 1990 or we will refund double the value!!
Only one of each item can be ordered at these prices.

Ref		
CB1	**1983 Machin** £1.30 U/M or FU **£5.50**, used	£1.95
	-do-Traffic Light gutter pair	£10.50
CB2	**1985 Machin** £1.41 fine used **£2.50**, comm used	£1.25
CB3	**1948 Silver Wedding** £1 U/M **£22**, fine used	£19.95
CB4	**1858 Queen Victoria** 1d. Red Collection 150 different plates, all good sound used copies. Complete ex. Plate 77	£198.00
CB5	**1840 1d. Black** SG1, a used copy with 3 margins	£29.00
CB6	**1988 Castle** High Values £1–£5.00 (4) good used	£2.75
CB7	**1984 Frama** labels, ½p–16p (32 values) unmounted	£15.00
	-do- Souvenir F.D.C.s (4), scarce	£17.50
CB8	**1984 Frama** labels – original 3 values in special Post Office Pres. Envelope	£1.25
CB9	**1984 Frama** labels – later values 16½p & 17p (2) U/M	£1.25
CB10	-do- on Souv. F.D.C. or PHQ Card First Day	£1.50
CB11	**1963 I.O.M.** 3d Chalky S.G.1M2a U/M	£9.95
CB12	**Mini-Collection** of 15 diff. G.B. postally valid S/Sheets	£10.50
CB13	**G.B. Exhibition S/Shts** 1960–1985 20 different	£6.50
CB14	**1937 Duke & Duchess of Windsor**, pair of original Wedding Day Covers with Monts (France) 3rd June 1937 postmark (normally £35.00) special price	£25.00
CB15	**50 diff.** Jersey/Guernsey & I.O.M. F.D.C.s to clear	£17.95
CB16	**65 diff.** G.B., C. Isles & I.O.M. airletters	£22.50
CB17	**1934 G.V.** Photo 10d, SG 448 fine used	£2.95
CB18	**1939 G.VI** 2/6 Brown, SG 476, sound used copy, our price only	£1.25
CB19	**1939 G.VI** 10/- Dark Blue, SG 478, sound used copy	£3.95
CB20	**1952 Tudor** ½d to 1/6, 17 values Complete, lightly mounted mint, SG 515/531	£19.50

All the above offers are postpaid (recorded delivery 30p, Registered £1.50 extra)

Send for a copy of our latest, 64 page, GB Price List

Phone 042128 2044, or fax 042128 2981

or write to

Rushstamps (Retail) Ltd., P.O. Box One, Lyndhurst, Hampshire SO43 7PP

WE ACCEPT TELEPHONE & CREDIT CARD ORDERS
WHY NOT TELEPHONE FOR YOUR FREE LIST NOW!! COMPARE AND SAVE!!

531 Oil—North Sea Production Platform

532 Coal—Modern Pithead

533 Natural Gas—Flame Rising from Sea

534 Electricity—Nuclear Power Station and Uranium Atom

Energy Resources

1978 (25 JAN.) *'All-over' phosphor*

1050	**531**	9p multicoloured ..	25	20	☐	☐
1051	**532**	10½p multicoloured ..	25	35	☐	☐
1052	**533**	11p multicoloured ..	35	40	☐	☐
1053	**534**	13p multicoloured ..	40	40	☐	☐
		Set of 4	1·10	1·10	☐	☐
		First Day Cover		1·25		☐
		Presentation Pack	2·00		☐	
		PHQ Cards (set of 4) ..	3·00	4·00	☐	☐
		Set of 4 Gutter Pairs	2·25		☐	
		Set of 4 Traffic Light				
		Gutter Pairs	4·00		☐	

535 Tower of London

536 Holyroodhouse

537 Caernarvon Castle

538 Hampton Court Palace

British Architecture (Historic Buildings)

1978 (1 MAR.) *'All-over' phosphor*

1054	**535**	9p multicoloured ..	25	20	☐	☐
1055	**536**	10½p multicoloured ..	25	30	☐	☐
1056	**537**	11p multicoloured ..	35	35	☐	☐
1057	**538**	13p multicoloured ..	40	40	☐	☐
		Set of 4	1·10	1·10	☐	☐
		First Day Cover		1·25		☐
		Presentation Pack	2·00		☐	
		PHQ Cards (set of 4)	3·00	3·50	☐	☐
		Set of 4 Gutter Pairs ..	2·25		☐	
		Set of 4 Traffic Light				
		Gutter Pairs	4·00		☐	
MS1058	121 ×90 mm. Nos. 1054/57		1·25	1·60	☐	☐
		First Day Cover		2·00		☐

P/O — £85

No. MS1058 was sold at 53½p, the premium being used for the London 1980 Stamp Exhibition.

539 State Coach

540 St Edward's Crown

541 The Sovereign's Orb

542 Imperial State Crown

25th Anniversary of Coronation

1978 (31 MAY) *'All-over' phosphor*

1059	**539**	9p gold and blue ..	20	20	☐	☐
1060	**540**	10½p gold and red ..	25	30	☐	☐
1061	**541**	11p gold and green ..	35	40	☐	☐
1062	**542**	13p gold and violet ..	40	40	☐	☐
		Set of 4	1·10	1·10	☐	☐
		First Day Cover		1·25		☐
		Presentation Pack	1·50		☐	
		Souvenir Book	4·00		☐	
		PHQ Cards (set of 4) ..	2·50	2·25	☐	☐
		Set of 4 Gutter Pairs ..	2·25		☐	
		Set of 4 Traffic Light				
		Gutter Pairs	4·00		☐	

543 Shire Horse

544 Shetland Pony

545 Welsh Pony

546 Thoroughbred

Horses

1978 (5 July) *'All-over' phosphor*

1063	**543**	9p multicoloured ..	20	25	☐	☐
1064	**544**	10½p multicoloured ..	25	30	☐	☐
1065	**545**	11p multicoloured ..	35	35	☐	☐
1066	**546**	13p multicoloured ..	40	40	☐	☐
		Set of 4	1·10	1·10	☐	☐
		First Day Cover		1·50		☐
		Presentation Pack	1·50		☐	
		PHQ Cards (set of 4)	2·50	3·50	☐	☐
		Set of 4 Gutter Pairs	2·25		☐	
		Set of 4 Traffic Light Gutter Pairs	4·00		☐	

547 Penny-farthing and 1884 Safety Bicycle

548 1920 Touring Bicycles

549 Modern Small-wheel Bicycles

550 1978 Road-racers

Centenaries of Cyclists Touring Club and British Cycling Federation

1978 (2 Aug.) *'All-over' phosphor*

1067	**547**	9p multicoloured ..	20	20	☐	☐
1068	**548**	10½p multicoloured ..	25	35	☐	☐
1069	**549**	11p multicoloured ..	35	35	☐	☐
1070	**550**	13p multicoloured ..	40	40	☐	☐
		Set of 4	1·10	1·10	☐	☐
		First Day Cover		1·25		☐
		Presentation Pack	1·50		☐	
		PHQ Cards (set of 4)	1·75	2·75	☐	☐
		Set of 4 Gutter Pairs	2·25		☐	
		Set of 4 Traffic Light Gutter Pairs	4·00		☐	

551 Singing Carols round the Christmas Tree

552 The Waits

553 18th-Century Carol Singers

554 'The Boar's Head Carol'

Christmas

1978 (22 Nov.) *One centre posphor band (7p) or 'all-over' phosphor (others)*

1071	**551**	7p multicoloured ..	20	20	☐	☐
1072	**552**	9p multicoloured ..	25	25	☐	☐
1073	**553**	11p multicoloured ..	30	35	☐	☐
1074	**554**	13p multicoloured ..	35	35	☐	☐
		Set of 4	1·00	1·00	☐	☐
		First Day Cover		1·00		☐
		Presentation Pack	1·40		☐	
		PHQ Cards (set of 4)	1·75	3·50	☐	☐
		Set of 4 Gutter Pairs	2·00		☐	
		Set of 4 Traffic Light Gutter Pairs	3·00		☐	

Collectors Pack 1978

1978 (22 Nov.) *Comprises Nos.* 1050/7. 1059/74

	Collectors Pack	7·00		☐

555 Old English Sheepdog

556 Welsh Springer Spaniel

557 West Highland Terrier

558 Irish Setter

Dogs

1979 (7 Feb.) *'All-over' phosphor*

1075	**555**	9p multicoloured ..	20	25	☐	☐
1076	**556**	10½p multicoloured ..	30	35	☐	☐
1077	**557**	11p multicoloured ..	35	40	☐	☐
1078	**558**	13p multicoloured ..	40	40	☐	☐
		Set of 4	1·10	1·25	☐	☐
		First Day Cover ..		1·25		☐
		Presentation Pack	1·50		☐	
		PHQ Cards (set of 4)	3·00	3·50	☐	☐
		Set of 4 Gutter Pairs ..	2·25		☐	
		Set of 4 Traffic Light				
		Gutter Pairs	3·75		☐	

559 Primrose

560 Daffodil

561 Bluebell

562 Snowdrop

Spring Wild Flowers

1979 (21 Mar.) *'All-over' phosphor*

1079	**559**	9p multicoloured ..	20	20	☐	☐
1080	**560**	10½p multicoloured ..	30	35	☐	☐
1081	**561**	11p multicoloured ..	35	40	☐	☐
1082	**562**	13p multicoloured ..	35	40	☐	☐
		Set of 4	1·10	1·10	☐	☐
		First Day Cover		1·25		☐
		Presentation Pack	1·50		☐	
		PHQ Cards (set of 4)	1·50	3·50	☐	☐
		Set of 4 Gutter Pairs ..	2·25		☐	
		Set of 4 Traffic Light				
		Gutter Pairs	3·75		☐	

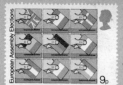

563

564

565

566

T **563/6** show hands placing the flags of the member nations into ballot boxes.

First Direct Elections to European Assembly

1979 (9 May) *Phosphorised paper*

1083	**563**	9p multicoloured ..	20	20	☐	☐
1084	**564**	10½p multicoloured ..	30	35	☐	☐
1085	**565**	11p multicoloured ..	35	40	☐	☐
1086	**566**	13p multicoloured ..	35	40	☐	☐
		Set of 4	1·10	1·10	☐	☐
		First Day Cover		1·25		☐
		Presentation Pack	1·50		☐	
		PHQ Cards (set of 4)	1·50	3·50	☐	☐
		Set of 4 Gutter Pairs ..	2·25		☐	
		Set of 4 Traffic Light				
		Gutter Pairs	3·75		☐	

567 'Saddling "Mahmoud" for the Derby, 1936' (Sir Alfred Munnings)

568 'The Liverpool Great National Steeple Chase, 1839' (aquatint by F. C. Turner)

569 'The First Spring Meeting, Newmarket, 1793' (J. N. Sartorius)

570 'Racing at Dorsett Ferry, Windsor, 1684' (Francis Barlow)

Horseracing Paintings and Bicentenary of The Derby (9p)

1979 (6 June) 'All-over' phosphor

1087	**567**	9p multicoloured . .	25	25	☐	☐
1088	**568**	10½p multicoloured ..	30	30	☐	☐
1089	**569**	11p multicoloured ..	35	35	☐	☐
1090	**570**	13p multicoloured ..	40	40	☐	☐
		Set of 4	1·10	1·10	☐	☐
		First Day Cover		1·25		☐
		Presentation Pack ..	1·50		☐	
		PHQ Cards (set of 4) ..	1·60	3·00	☐	☐
		Set of 4 Gutter Pairs ..	2·25		☐	
		Set of 4 Traffic Light Gutter Pairs	3·75		☐	

571 The Tale of Peter Rabbit (Beatrix Potter)

572 The Wind in the Willows (Kenneth Grahame)

573 Winnie-the-Pooh (A. A. Milne)

574 Alice's Adventures in Wonderland (Lewis Carroll)

T **571/4** depict original illustrations from the four books.

International Year of the Child

1979 (11 July) 'All-over' phosphor

1091	**571**	9p multicoloured ..	45	20	☐	☐
1092	**572**	10½p multicoloured ..	50	35	☐	☐
1093	**573**	11p multicoloured ..	55	40	☐	☐
1094	**574**	13p multicoloured ..	60	40	☐	☐
		Set of 4	1·90	1·25	☐	☐
		First Day Cover		1·25		☐
		Presentation Pack ..	2·25		☐	
		PHQ Cards (set of 4) ..	1·75	2·25	☐	☐
		Set of 4 Gutter Pairs ..	3·75		☐	
		Set of 4 Traffic Light Gutter Pairs	4·50		☐	

For full information on all future British issues, collectors should write to the British Post Office Philatelic Bureau, 20 Brandon Street, Edinburgh EH3 5TT

575 Sir Rowland Hill, 1795–1879

576 General Post, c. 1839

577 London Post, c. 1839

578 Uniform Postage, 1840

Death Centenary of Sir Rowland Hill (Postal Reformer)

1979 (22 Aug.–24 Oct.) 'All-over' phosphor

1095	**575**	10p multicoloured ..	25	25	☐	☐
1096	**576**	11½p multicoloured ..	30	35	☐	☐
1097	**577**	13p multicoloured ..	35	40	☐	☐
1098	**578**	15p multicoloured ..	40	40	☐	☐
		Set of 4	1·10	1·25	☐	☐
		First Day Cover		1·25		☐
		Presentation Pack	1·60		☐	
		PHQ Cards (set of 4) ..	1·50	2·25	☐	☐
		Set of 4 Gutter Pairs ..	2·40		☐	
		Set of 4 Traffic Light Gutter Pairs	3·75		☐	
MS1099	89×121 mm. Nos. 1095/8		1·10	1·25	☐	☐
	First Day Cover (24 Oct.)			1·25		☐

No. **MS**1099 was sold at 59½p, the premium being used for the London 1980 Stamp Exhibition.

579 Policeman on the Beat

580 Policeman directing Traffic

57

13P

15P

581 Mounted Policewoman

582 River Patrol Boat

150th Anniversary of Metropolitan Police

1979 (26 SEPT.) *Phosphorised paper*

1100	**579**	10p multicoloured ..	25	25	□	□
1101	**580**	11½p multicoloured ..	30	35	□	□
1102	**581**	13p multicoloured ..	35	40	□	□
1103	**582**	15p multicoloured ..	40	40	□	□
		Set of 4	1·10	1·25	□	□
		First Day Cover		1·25	□	
		Presentation Pack ..	1·60		□	
		PHQ Cards (set of 4) ..	1·50	2·25	□	□
		Set of 4 Gutter Pairs ..	2·40		□	
		Set of 4 Traffic Light				
		Gutter Pairs	3·75		□	

8½P

10P

583 The Three Kings

584 Angel appearing to the Shepherds

11½P

13P

585 The Nativity

586 Mary and Joseph travelling to Bethlehem

15P

587 The Annunciation

Christmas

1979 (21 Nov.) *One centre phosphor band (8p) or phosphorised paper (others)*

1104	**583**	8p multicoloured ...	20	20	□	□
1105	**584**	10p multicoloured ..	25	25	□	□
1106	**585**	11½p multicoloured ..	30	35	□	□
1107	**586**	13p multicoloured ..	40	40	□	□
1108	**587**	15p multicoloured ..	40	45	□	□
		Set of 5	1·40	1·50	□	□
		First Day Cover		1·50		□
		Presentation Pack ..	1·75		□	
		PHQ Cards (set of 5) ..	1·50	2·25	□	□
		Set of 5 Gutter Pairs ..	2·90		□	
		Set of 5 Traffic Light				
		Gutter Pairs	3·75		□	

Collectors Pack 1979

1979 (21 Nov.) *Comprises Nos. 1075/98, 1100/8*

	Collectors Pack	9·00	□

KINGFISHER 10P

DIPPER 11½P

588 Kingfisher

589 Dipper

MOORHEN 13P

YELLOW WAGTAIL 15P

590 Moorhen

591 Yellow Wagtails

Centenary of Wild Bird Protection Act

1980 (16 JAN.) *Phosphorised paper*

1109	**588**	10p multicoloured ..	25	25	□	□
1110	**589**	11½p multicoloured ..	30	35	□	□
1111	**590**	13p multicoloured ..	40	45	□	□
1112	**591**	15p multicoloured ..	45	50	□	□
		Set of 4	1·25	1·40	□	□
		First Day Cover		1·40		□
		Presentation Pack ..	1·75		□	
		PHQ Cards (set of 4) ..	1·50	2·25	□	□
		Set of 4 Gutter Pairs ..	2·50		□	

592 *Rocket* approaching Moorish Arch, Liverpool

593 First and Second Class Carriages passing through Olive Mount Cutting

594 Third Class Carriage and Cattle Truck crossing Chat Moss

595 Horsebox and Carriage Truck near Bridgewater Canal

596 Goods Truck and Mail-coach at Manchester

T **592/6** were printed together, *se-tenant* in horizontal strips of 5 throughout the sheet.

150th Anniversary of Liverpool and Manchester Railway

1980 (12 MAR.) *Phosphorised paper*

1113	**592**	12p multicoloured	25	25	☐	☐
	a.	Strip of 5.				
		Nos. 1113/17	1·50	1·60	☐	☐
1114	**593**	12p multicoloured	25	25	☐	☐
1115	**594**	12p multicoloured	25	25	☐	☐
1116	**595**	12p multicoloured	25	25	☐	☐
1117	**596**	12p multicoloured	25	25	☐	☐
		Set of 5	1·50	1·10	☐	☐
		First Day Cover		1·60		☐
		Presentation Pack	2·00		☐	
		PHQ Cards (*set of* 5)	1·60	3·00	☐	☐
		Gutter strip of 10	3·25		☐	

597 Montage of London Buildings

"London 1980" International Stamp Exhibition

1980 (9 APR–7 MAY) *Phosphorised paper. Perf* $14\frac{1}{2} \times 14$

1118	**597**	50p agate	1·50	1·25	☐	☐
		First Day Cover		1·25		☐
		Presentation Pack	1·75		☐	
		PHQ Card	50	1·60	☐	☐
		Gutter Pair	3·00		☐	
MS1119		90×123 mm. No. 1118	1·25	1·40	☐	☐
		First Day Cover (7 May)		1·40		☐

No. **MS**1119 was sold at 75p, the premium being used for the exhibition.

598 Buckingham Palace

599 The Albert Memorial

600 Royal Opera House

601 Hampton Court

17½p Kensington Palace

602 Kensington Palace

607 Queen Elizabeth the
Queen Mother

London Landmarks

1980 (7 MAY) *Phosphorised paper*

1120	**598**	10½p multicoloured	25	25	☐	☐
1121	**599**	12p multicoloured	30	30	☐	☐
1122	**600**	13½p multicoloured	35	35	☐	☐
1123	**601**	15p multicoloured	40	45	☐	☐
1124	**602**	17½p multicoloured	50	55	☐	☐
		Set of 5	1·60	1·75	☐	☐
		First Day Cover		1·75		☐
		Presentation Pack	2·10		☐	
		PHQ Cards (set of 5)	1·50	2·50	☐	☐
		Set of 5 Gutter Pairs	3·50		☐	

80th Birthday of Queen Elizabeth the Queen Mother

1980 (4 AUG.) *Phosphorised paper*

1129	**607**	12p multicoloured	35	35	☐	☐
		First Day Cover		60		☐
		PHQ Card	50	90	☐	☐
		Gutter Pair	75		☐	

603 Charlotte Bronte
(*Jane Eyre*)

604 George Eliot (*The Mill
on the Floss*)

608 Sir Henry Wood

609 Sir Thomas Beecham

605 Emily Bronte
(*Wuthering Heights*)

606 Mrs Gaskell (*North and
South*)

T 603/6 show authoresses and scenes from their novels. T 603/4 also
include the "Europa" C.E.P.T. emblem.

610 Sir Malcolm Sargent

611 Sir John Barbirolli

Famous Authoresses

1980 (9 JULY) *Phosphorised paper*

1125	**603**	12p multicoloured	30	30	☐	☐
1126	**604**	13½p multicoloured	35	35	☐	☐
1127	**605**	15p multicoloured	40	45	☐	☐
1128	**606**	17½p multicoloured	50	50	☐	☐
		Set of 4	1·40	1·40	☐	☐
		First Day Cover		1·40		☐
		Presentation Pack	1·90		☐	
		PHQ Cards (set of 4)	1·50	2·00	☐	☐
		Set of 4 Gutter Pairs	2·90		☐	

British Conductors

1980 (10 SEPT.) *Phosphorised paper*

1130	**608**	12p multicoloured	30	30	☐	☐
1131	**609**	13½p multicoloured	35	40	☐	☐
1132	**610**	15p multicoloured	45	45	☐	☐
1133	**611**	17½p multicoloured	50	50	☐	☐
		Set of 4	1·40	1·50	☐	☐
		First Day Cover		1·50		☐
		Presentation Pack	1·90		☐	
		PHQ Cards (set of 4)	1·50	2·00	☐	☐
		Set of 4 Gutter Pairs	2·90		☐	

612 Running

613 Rugby

614 Boxing

615 Cricket

618 Apples and Mistletoe

619 Crown, Chains and Bell

620 Holly

Sports Centenaries

1980 (10 Oct.) *Phosphorised paper. Perf 14 × 14½*

1134	612	12p multicoloured ..	30	30	☐	☐
1135	613	13½p multicoloured ..	35	40	☐	☐
1136	614	15p multicoloured ..	40	40	☐	☐
1137	615	17½p multicoloured ..	50	55	☐	☐
		Set of 4	1·40	1·50	☐	☐
		First Day Cover		1·50		☐
		Presentation Pack	1·90		☐	
		PHQ Cards (set of 4) ..	1·50	2·00	☐	☐
		Set of 4 Gutter Pairs	2·90		☐	

Centenaries:– 12p Amateur Athletics Association; 13½p Welsh Rugby Union; 15p Amateur Boxing Association; 17½p First England v Australia Test Match.

Christmas

1980 (19 Nov.) *One centre phosphor band (10p) or phosphorised paper (others)*

1138	616	10p multicoloured ..	25	25	☐	☐
1139	617	12p multicoloured ..	30	35	☐	☐
1140	618	13½p multicoloured ..	35	40	☐	☐
1141	619	15p multicoloured ..	40	45	☐	☐
1142	620	17½p multicoloured ..	45	50	☐	☐
		Set of 5	1·60	1·75	☐	☐
		First Day Cover..		1·75		☐
		Presentation Pack	2·10		☐	
		PHQ Cards (set of 5) ..	1·50	2·00	☐	☐
		Set of 5 Gutter Pairs ..	3·50		☐	

Collectors Pack 1980

1980 (19 Nov.) *Comprises Nos. 1109/18, 1120/42*

	Collectors Pack..	13·00	☐

616 Christmas Tree

617 Candles

621 St. Valentine's Day

622 Morris Dancers

623 Lammastide

624 Medieval Mummers

T **621/22** also include the "Europa" C.E.P.T. emblem.

Folklore

1981 (6 FEB.) *Phosphorised paper*

1143	**621**	14p multicoloured . .	35	35	☐	☐
1144	**622**	18p multicoloured . .	45	50	☐	☐
1145	**623**	22p multicoloured . .	60	60	☐	☐
1146	**624**	25p multicoloured . .	65	70	☐	☐
		Set of 4	1·90	2·00	☐	☐
		First Day Cover		2·00		☐
		Presentation Pack	2·40		☐	
		PHQ Cards (set of 4) . .	1·50	2·00	☐	☐
		Set of 4 Gutter Pairs	4·00		☐	

625 Blind Man with Guide Dog

626 Hands spelling "Deaf" in Sign Language

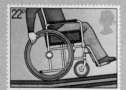

627 Disabled Man in Wheelchair

628 Disabled Artist painting with Foot

International Year of the Disabled

1981 (25 MAR.) *Phosphorised paper*

1147	**625**	14p multicoloured . .	35	35	☐	☐
1148	**626**	18p multicoloured . .	45	50	☐	☐
1149	**627**	22p multicoloured . .	60	60	☐	☐
1150	**628**	25p multicoloured . .	65	70	☐	☐
		Set of 4	1·90	2·00	☐	☐
		First Day Cover		2·00		☐
		Presentation Pack	2·40		☐	
		PHQ Cards (set of 4) . .	1·50	2·25	☐	☐
		Set of 4 Gutter Pairs	4·00		☐	

629 Small Tortoiseshell

630 Large Blue

631 Peacock

632 Chequered Skipper

Butterflies

1981 (13 MAY) *Phosphorised paper*

1151	**629**	14p multicoloured . .	35	35	☐	☐
1152	**630**	18p multicoloured . .	50	50	☐	☐
1153	**631**	22p multicoloured . .	60	65	☐	☐
1154	**632**	25p multicoloured . .	70	75	☐	☐
		Set of 4	2·00	2·00	☐	☐
		First Day Cover		2·00		☐
		Presentation Pack	2·50		☐	
		PHQ Cards (set of 4) . .	1·60	2·25	☐	☐
		Set of 4 Gutter Pairs	4·00		☐	

633 Glenfinnan, Scotland

634 Derwentwater, England

635 Stackpole Head, Wales

636 Giant's Causeway, N. Ireland

637 St Kilda, Scotland

50th Anniversary of National Trust for Scotland

1981 (24 JUNE) *Phosphorised paper*

1155	633	14p multicoloured ..	40	40	☐	☐
1156	634	18p multicoloured ..	50	55	☐	☐
1157	635	20p multicoloured ..	55	60	☐	☐
1158	636	22p multicoloured ..	60	60	☐	☐
1159	637	25p multicoloured ..	65	70	☐	☐
		Set of 5	2·40	2·50	☐	☐
		First Day Cover..		2·50		☐
		Presentation Pack	2·90		☐	
		PHQ Cards (set of 5)	2·00	2·75	☐	☐
		Set of 5 Gutter Pairs	5·00		☐	

638 Prince Charles and Lady Diana Spencer

Royal Wedding

1981 (22 JULY) *Phosphorised paper*

1160	638	14p multicoloured ..	35	35	☐	☐
1161		25p multicoloured ..	90	90	☐	☐
		Set of 2	1·25	1·25	☐	☐
		First Day Cover		2·00		☐
		Presentation Pack	1·75		☐	
		Souvenir Book	4·50		☐	
		PHQ Cards (set of 2)	1·00	2·00	☐	☐
		Set of 2 Gutter Pairs	2·50		☐	

639 "Expeditions"

640 "Skills"

641 "Service"

642 "Recreation"

25th Anniversary of Duke of Edinburgh Award Scheme

1981 (12 AUG.) *Phosphorised paper. Perf 14*

1162	639	14p multicoloured ..	35	35	☐	☐
1163	640	18p multicoloured ..	50	50	☐	☐
1164	641	22p multicoloured ..	60	60	☐	☐
1165	642	25p multicoloured ..	70	70	☐	☐
		Set of 4	2·00	2·00	☐	☐
		First Day Cover..		2·00		☐
		Presentation Pack	2·50		☐	
		PHQ Cards (set of 4)	1·60	2·25	☐	☐
		Set of 4 Gutter Pairs	4·00		☐	

643 Cockle-Dredging

644 Hauling Trawl Net

645 Lobster Potting

646 Hoisting Seine Net

Fishing Industry

1981 (23 SEPT.) *Phosphorised paper*

1166	643	14p multicoloured ..	35	35	☐	☐
1167	644	18p multicoloured ..	50	50	☐	☐
1168	645	22p multicoloured ..	60	60	☐	☐
1169	646	25p multicoloured ..	70	65	☐	☐
		Set of 4	2·00	2·00	☐	☐
		First Day Cover..		2·00		☐
		Presentation Pack	2·50		☐	
		PHQ Cards (set of 4)	2·00	2·25	☐	☐
		Set of 4 Gutter Pairs	4·00		☐	

Nos. 1166/9 were issued on the occasion of the centenary of Royal National Mission to Deep Sea Fishermen.

647 Father Christmas

648 Jesus Christ

649 Flying Angel

650 Joseph and Mary
arriving at Bethlehem

651 Three Kings approaching
Bethlehem

Christmas. Children's Pictures

1981 (18 NOV.) *One phosphor band (11½p) or phosphorised paper (others)*

1170	**647**	11½p multicoloured	..	30	30	☐	☐
1171	**648**	14p multicoloured	..	35	40	☐	☐
1172	**649**	18p multicoloured	..	45	50	☐	☐
1173	**650**	22p multicoloured	..	60	60	☐	☐
1174	**651**	25p multicoloured	..	65	70	☐	☐
		Set of 5		2·10	2·25	☐	☐
		First Day Cover ..	.. ..		2·25		☐
		Presentation Pack	.. ..	2·60		☐	
		PHO Cards (set of 5)	..	2·00	2·50	☐	☐
		Set of 5 Gutter Pairs	..	4·50		☐	

Collectors Pack 1981

1981 (18 NOV.) *Comprises Nos. 1143/74*

	Collectors Pack	..	..	20·00	☐

For full information on all future British issues, collectors should write to the British Post Office Philatelic Bureau, 20 Brandon Street, Edinburgh EH3 5TT.

652 Charles Darwin and Giant
Tortoises

653 Darwin and Marine
Iguanas

654 Darwin, Cactus Ground
Finch and Large Ground
Finch

655 Darwin and Prehistoric
Skulls

Death Centenary of Charles Darwin

1982 (10 FEB.) *Phosphorised paper*

1175	**652**	15½p multicoloured	..	35	35	☐
1176	**653**	19½p multicoloured	..	55	60	☐
1177	**654**	26p multicoloured	..	65	70	☐
1178	**655**	29p multicoloured	..	70	75	☐
		Set of 4		2·10	2·25	☐
		First Day Cover ..	.. ..		2·25	
		Presentation Pack	.. ..	2·60		☐
		PHQ Cards (set of 4)	..	2·50	4·50	☐
		Set of 4 Gutter Pairs	.. ..	4·50		☐

656 Boys' Brigade

657 Girls' Brigade

658 Boy Scout
Movement

659 Girl Guide
Movement

Youth Organizations

1982 (24 MAR.) *Phosphorised paper*

1179	**656**	15½p multicoloured	..	35	35	☐	☐
1180	**657**	19½p multicoloured	..	65	65	☐	☐
1181	**658**	26p multicoloured	..	90	90	☐	☐
1182	**659**	29p multicoloured	..	90	90	☐	☐
		Set of 4	.. .. ..	2·60	2·60	☐	☐
		First Day Cover ..	.. ..		2·60		☐
		Presentation Pack	.. ..	3·25		☐	
		PHQ Cards (set of 4)	..	2·50	3·00	☐	☐
		Set of 4 Gutter Pairs	..	5·25		☐	

Nos. 1179/82 were issued on the occasion of the 75th anniversary of the Boy Scout Movement, the 125th birth anniversary of Lord Baden-Powell and the centenary of the Boys' Brigade (1983).

660 Ballerina

661 'Harlequin'

662 'Hamlet'

663 Opera Singer

Europa. British Theatre

1982 (28 APR.) *Phosphorised paper*

1183	**660**	15½p multicoloured	..	35	35	☐	☐
1184	**661**	19½p multicoloured	..	60	70	☐	☐
1185	**662**	26p multicoloured	..	85	90	☐	☐
1186	**663**	29p multicoloured	..	90	1·00	☐	☐
		Set of 4	.. .. ..	2·50	2·75	☐	☐
		First Day Cover ..	.. ..		2·75		☐
		Presentation Pack	.. ..	3·00		☐	
		PHQ Cards (set of 4)	..	2·50	3·00	☐	☐
		Set of 4 Gutter Pairs	..	5·00		☐	

664 Henry VIII and *Mary Rose*

665 Admiral Blake and *Triumph*

666 Lord Nelson and HMS *Victory*

667 Lord Fisher and HMS *Dreadnought*

668 Viscount Cunningham and HMS *Warspite*

Maritime Heritage

1982 (16 JUNE) *Phosphorised paper*

1187	**664**	15½p multicoloured	..	35	35	☐	☐
1188	**665**	19½p multicoloured	..	70	60	☐	☐
1189	**666**	24p multicoloured	..	70	60	☐	☐
1190	**667**	26p multicoloured	..	80	70	☐	☐
1191	**668**	29p multicoloured	..	90	80	☐	☐
		Set of 5	.. ..	3·00	2·90	☐	☐
		First Day Cover ..	.. ..		2·90		☐
		Presentation Pack	.. ..	3·25		☐	
		PHQ Cards (set of 5)	..	3·00	3·50	☐	☐
		Set of 5 Gutter Pairs	..	6·00		☐	

669 "Strawberry Thief" (William Morris)

670 Untitled (Steiner and Co)

671 "Cherry Orchard" (Paul Nash)

672 "Chevron" (Andrew Foster)

British Textiles

1982 (23 JULY) *Phosphorised paper*

1192	**669**	15½p multicoloured ..	35	35	☐	☐
1193	**670**	19½p multicoloured ..	70	70	☐	☐
1194	**671**	26p multicoloured ..	70	70	☐	☐
1195	**672**	29p multicoloured ..	80	80	☐	☐
		Set of 4	2·40	2·40	☐	☐
		First Day Cover		2·40		☐
		Presentation Pack	2·90		☐	
		PHQ Cards (set of 4)	2·50	3·50	☐	☐
		Set of 4 Gutter Pairs ..	5·00		☐	

Nos 1192/5 were issued on the occasion of the 250th birth anniversary of Sir Richard Arkwright (inventor of spinning machine).

673 Development of Communications

674 Modern Technological Aids

Information Technology

1982 (8 SEPT.) *Phosphorised paper. Perf* 14×15

1196	**673**	15½p multicoloured ..	45	50	☐	☐
1197	**674**	26p multicoloured ..	80	85	☐	☐
		Set of 2	1·25	1·25	☐	☐
		First Day Cover		1·50		☐
		Presentation Pack	1·75		☐	
		PHQ Cards (set of 2) ..	1·50	3·50	☐	☐
		Set of 2 Gutter Pairs ..	2·50		☐	

675 Austin "Seven" and "Metro"

676 Ford "Model T" and "Escort"

677 Jaguar "SS1" and "XJ6"

678 Rolls-Royce "Silver Ghost" and "Silver Spirit"

British Motor Industry

1982 (13 OCT.) *Phosphorised paper.* Perf 14½×14

1198	**675**	15½p multicoloured ..	50	50	☐	☐
1199	**676**	19½p multicoloured ..	1·00	1·10	☐	☐
1200	**677**	26p multicoloured ..	1·10	1·25	☐	☐
1201	**678**	29p multicoloured ..	1·25	1·40	☐	☐
		Set of 4	3·50	3·75	☐	☐
		First Day Cover		3·75		☐
		Presentation Pack ..	4·00		☐	
		PHQ Cards (set of 4)	2·60	4·50	☐	☐
		Set of 4 Gutter Pairs	7·00		☐	

679 "While Shepherds Watched"

680 "The Holly and the Ivy"

681 "I Saw Three Ships"

682 "We Three Kings"

683 "Good King Wenceslas"

Christmas. Carols

1982 (17 Nov) *One phosphor band* (12½p) *or phosphorised paper* (*others*)

1202	**679**	12½p multicoloured	..	30	30	☐ ☐
1203	**680**	15½p multicoloured	..	55	45	☐ ☐
1204	**681**	19½p multicoloured	..	80	65	☐ ☐
1205	**682**	26p multicoloured	..	80	65	☐ ☐
1206	**683**	29p multicoloured	..	90	80	☐ ☐
		Set of 5	.. .. ..	3·00	2·50	☐ ☐
		First Day Cover	.. ..		2·50	☐
		Presentation Pack	.. ..	3·50		☐
		PHQ Cards (set of 5)	.. ..	3·00	4·50	☐ ☐
		Set of 5 Gutter Pairs	.. ..	6·00		☐

Collectors Pack 1982

1982 (17 Nov.) *Comprises Nos.* 1175/1206

	Collectors Pack	.. .. ..	24·00	☐

684 Salmon   685 Pike

686 Trout   687 Perch

British River Fishes

1983 (26 Jan.) *Phosphorised paper*

1207	**684**	15½p multicoloured	..	35	35	☐ ☐
1208	**685**	19½p multicoloured	..	65	65	☐ ☐
1209	**686**	26p multicoloured	..	65	65	☐ ☐
1210	**687**	29p multicoloured	..	75	75	☐ ☐
		Set of 4	.. .. ..	2·25	2·25	☐ ☐
		First Day Cover	.. ..		2·50	☐
		Presentation Pack	.. ..	3·00		☐
		PHQ Cards (set of 4)	.. ..	2·50	4·50	☐ ☐
		Set of 4 Gutter Pairs	.. ..	4·75		☐

688 Tropical Island   689 Desert

690 Temperate Farmland   691 Mountain Range

Commonwealth Day. Geographical Regions

1983 (9 Mar.) *Phosphorised paper*

1211	**688**	15½p multicoloured	..	35	40	☐ ☐
1212	**689**	19½p multicoloured	..	65	70	☐ ☐
1213	**690**	26p multicoloured	..	65	70	☐ ☐
1214	**691**	29p multicoloured	..	75	80	☐ ☐
		Set of 4	.. .. ..	2·25	2·40	☐ ☐
		First Day Cover	.. ..		2·50	☐
		Presentation Pack	.. ..	3·00		☐
		PHQ Cards (set of 4)	.. ..	2·50	4·50	☐ ☐
		Set of 4 Gutter Pairs	.. ..	4·75		☐

692 Humber Bridge   693 Thames Flood Barrier

694 Iolair (oilfield emergency support vessel)

Europa. Engineering Achievements

1983 (25 MAY) *Phosphorised paper.*

1215	**692**	16p multicoloured	..	50	45	□ □
1216	**693**	20½p multicoloured	..	1·40	1·25	□ □
1217	**694**	28p multicoloured	..	1·40	1·25	□ □
		Set of 3	..	3·00	2·60	□ □
		First Day Cover			2·60	□
		Presentation Pack	..	3·50		□
		PHQ Cards (set of 3) ..	..	2·50	3·75	□ □
		Set of 3 Gutter Pairs	..	6·00		□

British Army Uniforms

1983 (6 JULY) *Phosphorised paper.*

1218	**695**	16p multicoloured	..	40	40	□ □
1219	**696**	20½p multicoloured	..	70	70	□ □
1220	**697**	26p multicoloured	..	95	80	□ □
1221	**698**	28p multicoloured	..	1·00	80	□ □
1222	**699**	31p multicoloured	..	1·10	90	□ □
		Set of 5	..	3·75	3·25	□ □
		First Day Cover			3·25	□
		Presentation Pack	..	4·00		□
		PHQ Cards (set of 5) ..	..	4·00	5·00	□ □
		Set of 5 Gutter Pairs	..	7·50		□

Nos. 1218/22 were issued on the occasion of the 350th anniversary of The Royal Scots, the senior line regiment of the British Army.

695 Musketeer and Pikeman. The Royal Scots (1633)

696 Fusilier and Ensign. The Royal Welch Fusiliers (mid-18th century)

697 Riflemen. 96th Rifles (The Royal Green Jackets) (1805)

698 Sergeant (khaki service uniform) and Guardsman (full dress). The Irish Guards (1900)

700 20th-Century Garden, Sissinghurst

701 19th-Century Garden, Biddulph Grange

702 18th-Century Garden, Blenheim

703 17th-Century Garden, Pitmedden

699 Paratroopers. The Parachute Regiment (1983)

British Gardens

1983 (24 AUG.) *Phosphorised paper. Perf* 14

1223	**700**	16p multicoloured	..	40	40	□ □
1224	**701**	20½p multicoloured	..	50	55	□ □
1225	**702**	28p multicoloured	..	85	90	□ □
1226	**703**	31p multicoloured	..	90	90	□ □
		Set of 4	..	2·50	2·50	□ □
		First Day Cover	..		2·75	□
		Presentation Pack	..	3·25		□
		PHQ Cards (set of 4) ..	..	2·50	4·50	□ □
		Set of 4 Gutter Pairs	..	5·00		□

704 Merry-go-round

705 Big Wheel, Helter-skelter and Performing Animals

706 Side-shows

707 Early Produce Fair

British Fairs

1983 (5 OCT.) *Phosphorised paper.*

1227	**704**	16p multicoloured	..	40	40	□ □
1228	**705**	20½p multicoloured	..	50	55	□ □
1229	**706**	28p multicoloured	..	85	90	□ □
1230	**707**	31p multicoloured	..	90	90	□ □
	Set of 4	.. .. ..	..	2·50	2·50	□ □
	First Day Cover	.. ..	..		2·75	□
	Presentation Pack	..	..	3·25		□
	PHQ Cards (set of 4)	..	..	2·50	4·50	□ □
	Set of 4 Gutter Pairs		.. ..	5·00		□

Nos. 1227/30 were issued to mark the 850th Anniversary of St. Bartholomew's Fair, Smithfield, London.

708 "Christmas Post" (pillar-box)

709 "The Three Kings" (chimney-pots)

710 "World at Peace" (Dove and Blackbird)

711 "Light of Christmas" (street lamp)

712 "Christmas Dove" (hedge sculpture)

Christmas

1983 (16 NOV.) *One phosphor band* (12½p) *or phosphorised paper* (*others*)

1231	**708**	12½p multicoloured	..	30	30	□ □
1232	**709**	16p multicoloured	..	45	45	□ □
1233	**710**	20½p multicoloured	..	75	60	□ □
1234	**711**	28p multicoloured	..	1·00	90	□ □
1235	**712**	31p multicoloured	..	1·10	90	□ □
	Set of 5	.. ..	..	3·25	2·75	□ □
	First Day Cover	.. ..	..		2·75	□
	Presentation Pack	..	..	3·50		□
	PHQ Cards (set of 5)	..	..	3·00	4·50	□ □
	Set of 5 Gutter Pairs		..	6·50		□

Collectors Pack 1983

1983 (16 NOV.) *Comprises Nos.* 1207/35

	Collectors Pack	..	..	36·00	□

713 Arms of the College of Arms

714 Arms of King Richard III (founder)

715 Arms of the Earl Marshal of England

716 Arms of the City of London

500th Anniversary of College of Arms

1984 (17 Jan) Phosphorised paper. Perf 14½

1236	**713**	16p multicoloured		40	40	☐	☐
1237	**714**	20½p multicoloured		60	70	☐	☐
1238	**715**	28p multicoloured		85	90	☐	☐
1239	**716**	31p multicoloured		90	90	☐	☐
		Set of 4	..	2·60	2·60	☐	☐
		First Day Cover	..		2·75	☐	
		Presentation Pack	..	3·25		☐	
		PHQ Cards (set of 4)	..	2·50	5·00	☐	☐
		Set of 4 Gutter Pairs	..	5·25		☐	

717 Highland Cow

718 Chillingham Wild Bull

719 Hereford Bull

720 Welsh Black Bull

721 Irish Moiled Cow

British Cattle

1984 (6 Mar.) Phosphorised paper.

1240	**717**	16p multicoloured		40	40	☐	☐
1241	**718**	20½p multicoloured		65	65	☐	☐
1242	**719**	26p multicoloured		70	70	☐	☐
1243	**720**	28p multicoloured		85	85	☐	☐
1244	**721**	31p multicoloured		90	90	☐	☐
		Set of 5	..	3·25	3·00	☐	☐
		First Day Cover	..		3·50	☐	
		Presentation Pack	..	4·00		☐	
		PHQ Cards (set of 5)	..	3·00	5·00	☐	☐
		Set of 5 Gutter Pairs	..	6·50		☐	

Nos. 1240/4 marked the centenary of the Highland Cattle Society and the bicentenary of the Royal Highland and Agricultural Society of Scotland.

722 Festival Hall, Liverpool

723 Milburngate Shopping Centre, Durham

724 Bush House, Bristol

725 Commercial Street Housing Scheme, Perth

Urban Renewal

1984 (10 Apr.) Phosphorised paper.

1245	**722**	16p multicoloured	..	40	40	☐	☐
1246	**723**	20½p multicoloured	..	60	60	☐	☐
1247	**724**	28p multicoloured	..	90	90	☐	☐
1248	**725**	31p multicoloured	..	90	1·00	☐	☐
		Set of 4	..	2·50	2·60	☐	☐
		First Day Cover	..		3·00	☐	
		Presentation Pack	..	3·25		☐	
		PHQ Cards (set of 4)	..	2·50	5·00	☐	☐
		Set of 4 Gutter Pairs	..	5·00		☐	

Nos. 1245/8 mark the opening of the International Gardens Festival, Liverpool, and the 150th anniversaries of the Royal Institute of British Architects and the Chartered Institute of Building.

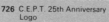

726 C.E.P.T. 25th Anniversary Logo

727 Abduction of Europa

Nos. 1249/50 and 1251/2 were each printed together, se-tenant, in horizontal pairs throughout the sheets.

Europa. 25th Anniversary of C.E.P.T. and 2nd European Parliamentary Elections

1984 (15 MAY) *Phosphorised paper.*

1249	**726**	16p	greenish slate, dp blue and gold ..	40	40	□	□
	a.		*Horiz pair. Nos. 1249/50* ..	1·00	1·00	□	□
1250	**727**	16p	greenish slate, dp bl, blk and gold ..	40	40	□	□
1251	**726**	20½p	Venetian red, deep magenta and gold ..	55	60	□	□
	a.		*Horizontal pair. Nos. 1251/2* ..	1·40	1·40	□	□
1252	**727**	20½p	Venetian red, deep magenta, black and gold ..	55	60	□	□
		Set of 4		2·25	1·75	□	□
		First Day Cover			3·00		□
		Presentation Pack		3·00			□
		PHQ Cards (set of 4) ..		2·50	5·00	□	□
		Set of 4 Gutter Pairs		4·50			□

728 Lancaster House

London Economic Summit Conference

1984 (5 JUNE) *Phosphorised paper.*

1253	**728**	31p	multicoloured ..	95	85	□	□
		First Day Cover			2·00		□
		PHQ Card		50	1·60	□	□
		Gutter Pair		1·90			□

729 View of Earth from "Apollo 11"

730 Navigational Chart of English Channel

731 Greenwich Observatory

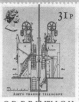

732 Sir George Airey's Transit Telescope

Centenary of Greenwich Meridian

1984 (26 JUNE) *Phosphorised paper. Perf* 14 × 14½

1254	**729**	16p	multicoloured ..	40	40	□	□
1255	**730**	20½p	multicoloured ..	60	60	□	□
1256	**731**	28p	multicoloured ..	90	80	□	□
1257	**732**	31p	multicoloured ..	95	90	□	□
		Set of 4		2·60	2·50	□	□
		First Day Cover			3·25		□
		Presentation Pack		3·25			□
		PHQ Cards (set of 4) ..		2·50	5·50	□	□
		Set of 4 Gutter Pairs ..		5·25			□

733 Bath Mail Coach, 1784

734 Attack on Exeter Mail, 1816

735 Norwich Mail in Thunderstorm, 1827

736 Holyhead and Liverpool Mails leaving London, 1828

737 Edinburgh Mail Snowbound, 1831

T **733/7** were printed together, *se-tenant* in horizontal strips of 5 throughout the sheet.

Bicentenary of First Mail Coach Run, Bath and Bristol to London

1984 (31 JULY) *Phosphorised paper*

1258	**733**	16p multicoloured	..	40	40	☐	☐
		a. Horiz strip of 5.					
		Nos. 1258/62	..	2·25	2·50	☐	☐
1259	**734**	16p multicoloured	..	40	40	☐	☐
1260	**735**	16p multicoloured	..	40	40	☐	☐
1261	**736**	16p multicoloured	..	40	40	☐	☐
1262	**737**	16p multicoloured	..	40	40	☐	☐
		Set of 5	..	2·25	1·75	☐	☐
		First Day Cover	..		3·00		☐
		Presentation Pack	..	3·00		☐	
		Souvenir Book	..	6·00		☐	
		PHQ Cards (set of 5)	..	3·00	5·00	☐	☐
		Gutter Strip of 10	..	4·75		☐	

738 Nigerian Clinic

739 Violinist and Acropolis, Athens

740 Building Project, Sri Lanka

741 British Council Library

50th Anniversary of The British Council

1984 (25 SEPT.) *Phosphorised paper*

1263	**738**	17p multicoloured	..	40	40	☐	☐
1264	**739**	22p multicoloured	..	60	65	☐	☐
1265	**740**	31p multicoloured	..	1·00	1·00	☐	☐
1266	**741**	34p multicoloured	..	1·00	1·00	☐	☐
		Set of 4	..	2·75	2·75	☐	☐
		First Day Cover	..		3·00		☐
		Presentation Pack	..	3·50		☐	
		PHQ Cards (set of 4)	..	2·50	4·50	☐	☐
		Set of 4 Gutter Pairs	..	5·50		☐	

For full information on all future British issues, collectors should write to the British Post Office Philatelic Bureau, 20 Brandon Street, Edinburgh EH3 5TT.

742 The Holy Family

743 Arrival in Bethlehem

744 Shepherd and Lamb

745 Virgin and Child

746 Offering of Frankincense

Christmas

1984 (20 Nov.) *One phosphor band (13p) or phosphorised paper (others)*

1267	**742**	13p multicoloured	..	30	30	☐	☐
1268	**743**	17p multicoloured	..	40	45	☐	☐
1269	**744**	22p multicoloured	..	55	60	☐	☐
1270	**745**	31p multicoloured	..	1·00	1·10	☐	☐
1271	**746**	34p multicoloured	..	1·00	1·10	☐	☐
		Set of 5	..	3·00	3·25	☐	☐
		First Day Cover	..		3·25		☐
		Presentation Pack	..	3·75		☐	
		PHQ Cards (set of 5)	..	3·00	4·50	☐	☐
		Set of 5 Gutter Pairs	..	6·00		☐	

Collectors Pack 1984

1984 (20 Nov.) *Comprises Nos. 1236/71*

	Collectors Pack	..	36·00	☐

Post Office Yearbook

1984 *Comprises Nos. 1236/71 in hardbound book with slip case.*

	Yearbook	..	55·00	☐

47 "The Flying Scotsman" 748 "The Golden Arrow"

754 Wart-Biter Bush-Cricket 755 Stag Beetle

49 "The Cheltenham Flyer" 750 "The Royal Scot"

756 Emperor Dragonfly

751 "The Cornish Riviera"

Insects

1985 (12 March) *Phosphorised paper*

1277	**752**	17p multicoloured	..	50	55	☐	☐
1278	**753**	22p multicoloured	..	70	70	☐	☐
1279	**754**	29p multicoloured	..	90	90	☐	☐
1280	**755**	31p multicoloured	..	1·10	1·10	☐	☐
1281	**756**	34p multicoloured	..	1·10	1·10	☐	☐
		Set of 5	..	4·00	4·00	☐	☐
		First Day Cover	..		4·25	☐	
		Presentation Pack	..	4·75		☐	
		PHQ Cards (set of 5) ..	..	3·00	5·50	☐	☐
		Set of 5 Gutter Pairs ..	..	8·00		☐	

Nos. 1277/81 were issued on the occasion of the centenaries of the Royal Entomological Society of London's Royal Charter and of the Selborne Society.

Famous Trains

1985 (22 Jan.) *Phosphorised paper*

1272	**747**	17p multicoloured	..	70	80	☐	☐
1273	**748**	22p multicoloured	..	90	90	☐	☐
1274	**749**	29p multicoloured	..	1·25	1·25	☐	☐
1275	**750**	31p multicoloured	..	1·25	1·25	☐	☐
1276	**751**	34p multicoloured	..	1·40	1·40	☐	☐
		Set of 5	..	5·00	5·00	☐	☐
		First Day Cover	..		7·00		☐
		Presentation Pack	..	6·00		☐	
		PHQ Cards (set of 5) ..	..	3·50	11·00	☐	☐
		Set of 5 Gutter Pairs ..	..	10·00		☐	

Nos. 1272/6 were issued on the occasion of the 150th anniversary of the Great Western Railway Company.

752 Buff Tailed Bumble Bee 753 Seven Spotted Ladybird 757 "Water Music", by Handel 758 "The Planets", by Holst

759 "The First Cuckoo", by Delius

760 "Sea Pictures", by Elgar

Europa – European Music Year

1985 (14 May) *Phosphorised paper. Perf 14½*

1282	757	17p multicoloured	..	50	40	☐	☐
1283	758	22p multicoloured	..	70	70	☐	☐
1284	759	31p multicoloured	..	1·10	1·10	☐	☐
1285	760	34p multicoloured	..	1·10	1·10	☐	☐
		Set of 4	.. .. ..	3·00	3·00	☐	☐
		First Day Cover	.. ..		3·75		☐
		Presentation Pack	.. ..	3·50		☐	
		PHQ Cards (set of 4)	.. ..	2·50	5·25	☐	☐
		Set of 4 Gutter Pairs	..	6·00		☐	

Nos. 1282/5 were issued on the occasion of the 300th birth anniversary of Handel.

761 R.N.L.I. Lifeboat and Signal Flags

762 Beachy Head Lighthouse and Chart

763 "Marecs A" Communications Satellite and Dish Aerials

764 Buoys

Safety at Sea

1985 (18 June) *Phosphorised paper. Perf 14*

1286	761	17p multicoloured	..	50	50	☐	☐
1287	762	22p multicoloured	..	70	70	☐	☐
1288	763	31p multicoloured	..	1·10	1·10	☐	☐
1289	764	34p multicoloured	..	1·10	1·10	☐	☐
		Set of 4	.. .. ..	3·00	3·00	☐	☐
		First Day Cover	.. ..		3·75		☐
		Presentation Pack	.. ..	3·50		☐	
		PHQ Cards (set of 4)	.. ..	2·50	5·25	☐	☐
		Set of 4 Gutter Pairs	..	6·00		☐	

Nos. 1286/9 were issued on the occasion of the bicentenary of the unimmersible lifeboat and the 50th anniversary of Radar.

765 Datapost Motorcyclist, City of London

766 Rural Postbus

767 Parcel Delivery in Winter

768 Town Letter Delivery

350 Years of Royal Mail Public Postal Service

1985 (30 July) *Phosphorised paper*

1290	765	17p multicoloured	..	45	45	☐	☐
1291	766	22p multicoloured	..	70	70	☐	☐
1292	767	31p multicoloured	..	1·10	1·10	☐	☐
1293	768	34p multicoloured	..	1·10	1·10	☐	☐
		Set of 4	.. .. ..	3·00	3·00	☐	☐
		First Day Cover	.. ..		3·75		☐
		Presentation Pack	.. ..	3·50		☐	
		PHQ Cards (set of 4)	.. ..	2·50	5·25	☐	☐
		Set of 4 Gutter Pairs	..	6·00		☐	

769 King Arthur and Merlin

770 The Lady of the Lake

771 Queen Guinevere and Sir Lancelot

772 Sir Galahad

777 Alfred Hitchcock (from photo by Howard Coster)

Arthurian Legends

1985 (3 SEPT.) *Phosphorised paper*

1294	**769**	17p multicoloured	..	40	40	☐	☐
1295	**770**	22p multicoloured	..	65	70	☐	☐
1296	**771**	31p multicoloured	..	1·10	1·10	☐	☐
1297	**772**	34p multicoloured	..	1·10	1·10	☐	☐
		Set of 4	..	3·00	3·00	☐	☐
		First Day Cover			3·75		☐
		Presentation Pack		3·50		☐	
		PHQ Cards (set of 4) ..	..	2·50	5·25	☐	☐
		Set of 4 Gutter Pairs		6·00		☐	

Nos. 1294/7 were issued on the occasion of the 500th anniversary of the printing of Sir Thomas Malory's *Morte d'Arthur*.

British Film Year

1985 (8 OCT.) *Phosphorised paper. Perf 14½*

1298	**773**	17p multicoloured	..	40	40	☐	☐
1299	**774**	22p multicoloured	..	70	80	☐	☐
1300	**775**	29p multicoloured	..	1·10	90	☐	☐
1301	**776**	31p multicoloured	..	1·10	1·10	☐	☐
1302	**777**	34p multicoloured	..	1·10	1·10	☐	☐
		Set of 5		4·00	4·00	☐	☐
		First Day Cover			5·00		☐
		Presentation Pack		4·25		☐	
		Souvenir Book		7·00		☐	
		PHQ Cards (set of 5) ..		2·75	5·75	☐	☐
		Set of 5 Gutter Pairs		8·00		☐	

773 Peter Sellers (from photo by Bill Brandt)

774 David Niven (from photo by Cornell Lucas)

775 Charlie Chaplin (from photo by Lord Snowdon)

776 Vivien Leigh (from photo by Angus McBean)

778 Principal Boy

779 Genie

780 Dame

781 Good Fairy

782 Pantomime Cat

Christmas. Pantomime Characters

1985 (19 Nov.) *One phosphor band (12p) or phosphorised paper (others)*

1303	**778**	12p multicoloured	..	35	35	☐	☐
1304	**779**	17p multicoloured	..	45	50	☐	☐
1305	**780**	22p multicoloured	..	65	65	☐	☐
1306	**781**	31p multicoloured	..	90	90	☐	☐
1307	**782**	34p multicoloured	..	1·00	1·00	☐	☐
		Set of 5	.. .. ..	3·00	3·00	☐	☐
		First Day Cover	.. ..		3·75		☐
		Presentation Pack	.. ..	4·00		☐	
		PHQ Cards (Set of 5)	..	2·75	5·50	☐	☐
		Set of 5 Gutter Pairs	..	6·00		☐	

Collectors Pack 1985

1985 (19 Nov.) *Comprises Nos. 1272/1307*

Collectors Pack	.. .. ..	36·00	☐

Post Office Yearbook

1985 *Comprises Nos. 1272/1307 in hardbound book with slip case.*

Yearbook	.. ..	75·00	☐

783 Light Bulb and North Sea Oil Drilling Rig (Energy)

784 Thermometer and Pharmaceutical Laboratory (Health)

785 Garden Hoe and Steel Works (Steel)

786 Loaf of Bread and Cornfield (Agriculture)

Industry Year

1986 (14 JAN.) *Phosphorised paper. Perf 14½ × 14*

1308	**783**	17p multicoloured	..	45	45	☐	☐
1309	**784**	22p multicoloured	..	90	70	☐	☐
1310	**785**	31p multicoloured	..	1·25	1·10	☐	☐
1311	**786**	34p multicoloured	..	1·25	1·10	☐	☐
		Set of 4	..	3·50	3·00	☐	☐
		First Day Cover	.. ..		4·50		☐
		Presentation Pack	..	3·50		☐	
		PHQ Cards (set of 4)	..	2·25	5·50	☐	☐
		Set of 4 Gutter Pairs	..	7·00		☐	

787 Dr. Edmond Halley as Comet

788 *Giotto* Spacecraft approaching Comet

789 "Twice in a Lifetime"

790 Comet orbiting Sun and Planets

Appearance of Halley's Comet

1986 (18 FEB.) *Phosphorised paper.*

1312	**787**	17p multicoloured	..	45	45	☐	☐
1313	**788**	22p multicoloured	..	90	70	☐	☐
1314	**789**	31p multicoloured	..	1·25	1·00	☐	☐
1315	**790**	34p multicoloured	..	1·25	1·10	☐	☐
		Set of 4	..	3·50	3·00	☐	☐
		First Day Cover	.. ..		5·00		☐
		Presentation Pack	..	3·50		☐	
		PHQ Cards (set of 4)	..	2·50	5·25	☐	☐
		Set of 4 Gutter Pairs	..	7·00		☐	

791 Queen Elizabeth II in 1928, 1942 and 1952

792 Queen Elizabeth II in 1958, 1973 and 1982

Nos. 1316/17 and 1318/19 were each printed together, *se-tenant*, in horizontal pairs throughout the sheets.

60th Birthday of Queen Elizabeth II

1986 (21 APR.) *Phosphorised paper.*

1316	**791**	17p multicoloured	..	60	50	☐	☐
		a. Horiz pair.					
		Nos.1316/17		1·60	1·50	☐	☐
1317	**792**	17p multicoloured	..	60	50	☐	☐
1318	**791**	34p multicoloured	..	1·10	1·00	☐	☐
		a. Horiz pair.					
		Nos.1318/19		2·50	2·40	☐	☐
1319	**792**	34p multicoloured	..	1·10	1·00	☐	☐
		Set of 4	..	3·75	2·50	☐	☐
		First Day Cover	.. ..		4·50		☐
		Presentation Pack	..	4·00		☐	
		Souvenir Book	..	7·00		☐	
		PHQ Cards (set of 4)	..	2·50	5·50	☐	☐
		Set of 4 Gutter Pairs	..	7·50		☐	

93 Barn Owl

794 Pine Marten

95 Wild Cat

796 Natterjack Toad

Europa. Nature Conservation. Endangered Species

986 (20 May) *Phosphorised paper. Perf* $14\frac{1}{2} \times 14$

320	**793**	17p multicoloured		50	55	☐ ☐
321	**794**	22p multicoloured		90	80	☐ ☐
322	**795**	31p multicoloured		1·25	1·25	☐ ☐
323	**796**	34p multicoloured		1·25	1·25	☐ ☐
		Set of 4		3·50	3·50	☐ ☐
		First Day Cover			4·50	☐
		Presentation Pack		4·00		☐
		PHQ Cards (set of 4)		2·00	5·25	☐ ☐
		Set of 4 Gutter Pairs		7·00		☐

97 Peasants working in Fields

798 Freemen working at Town Trades

99 Knight and Retainers

800 Lord at Banquet

900th Anniversary of Domesday Book

1986 (17 June) *Phosphorised paper*

1324	**797**	17p multicoloured		50	50	☐ ☐
1325	**798**	22p multicoloured		90	70	☐ ☐
1326	**799**	31p multicoloured		1·25	1·00	☐ ☐
1327	**800**	34p multicoloured		1·25	1·10	☐ ☐
		Set of 4		3·50	3·00	☐ ☐
		First Day Cover			3·75	☐
		Presentation Pack		4·00		☐
		PHQ Cards (set of 4)		2·00	5·00	☐ ☐
		Set of 4 Gutter Pairs		7·00		☐

801 Athletics

802 Rowing

803 Weightlifting

804 Rifle-Shooting

805 Hockey

Thirteenth Commonwealth Games, Edinburgh (Nos. 1328/31) and World Men's Hockey Cup, London (No. 1332)

1986 (15 July) *Phosphorised paper.*

1328	**801**	17p multicoloured		45	50	☐ ☐
1329	**802**	22p multicoloured		90	60	☐ ☐
1330	**803**	29p multicoloured		1·10	90	☐ ☐
1331	**804**	31p multicoloured		1·25	1·10	☐ ☐
1332	**805**	34p multicoloured		1·25	1·10	☐ ☐
		Set of 5		4·50	3·75	☐ ☐
		First Day Cover			5·50	☐
		Presentation Pack		5·25		☐
		PHQ Cards (Set of 5)		2·40	5·75	☐ ☐
		Set of 5 Gutter Pairs		9·00		☐

No. 1332 also marked the centenary of the Hockey Association.

806 Prince Andrew and Miss Sarah Ferguson 807

Royal Wedding

1986 (22 July) *One side band (12p) or phosphorised paper (17p)*

1333	806	12p multicoloured	..	50	40	☐	☐
1334	807	17p multicoloured	..	75	55	☐	☐
		Set of 2		1·25	90	☐	☐
		First Day Cover			2·50		☐
		Presentation Pack		1·60		☐	
		PHQ Cards (set of 2)	..	1·00	3·00	☐	☐
		Set of 2 Gutter Pairs	..	2·50		☐	

808 Stylised Cross on Ballot Paper

32nd Commonwealth Parliamentary Conference, London

1986 (19 Aug.) *Phosphorised paper. Perf 14 × 14½*

1335	808	34p multicoloured	..	1·10	90	☐	☐
		First Day Cover			1·60		☐
		PHQ Card		50	1·75	☐	☐
		Gutter Pair		2·25		☐	

809 Lord Dowding and "Hurricane"   810 Lord Tedder and "Typhoon"

811 Lord Trenchard and "DH 9A"   812 Sir Arthur Harris and "Lancaster"

813 Lord Portal and "Mosquito"

History of the Royal Air Force

1986 (16th Sept.) *Phosphorised paper. Perf 14½ × 14.*

1336	809	17p multicoloured	..	40	40	☐	☐
1337	810	22p multicoloured	..	90	70	☐	☐
1338	811	29p multicoloured	..	1·10	1·00	☐	☐
1339	812	31p multicoloured	..	1·25	1·00	☐	☐
1340	813	34p multicoloured	..	1·25	1·00	☐	☐
		Set of 5		4·50	3·75	☐	☐
		First Day Cover ..			4·50		☐
		Presentation Pack	..	5·25		☐	
		PHQ Cards (set of 5)		2·50	5·75	☐	☐
		Set of 5 Gutter Pairs	..	9·00		☐	

Nos. 1336/40 were issued to celebrate the 50th anniversary of the first R.A.F. Commands.

814 The Glastonbury Thorn   815 The Tanad Valley Plygain

816 The Hebrides Tribute   817 The Dewsbury Church Kne

818 The Hereford Boy Bishop

Christmas. Folk Customs

1986 One phosphor band (12p, 13p) or phosphorised paper (others)

1341	**814**	12p mult. (2 Dec.)	..	75	40	☐ ☐
1342		13p mult. (18 Nov.)	..	40	40	☐ ☐
1343	**815**	18p mult. (18 Nov.)	..	55	55	☐ ☐
1344	**816**	22p mult. (18 Nov.)	..	75	65	☐ ☐
1345	**817**	31p mult. (18 Nov.)	..	1·00	80	☐ ☐
1346	**818**	34p mult. (18 Nov.)	..	1·00	90	☐ ☐
		Set of 6	..	4·00	3·50	☐ ☐
		First Day Covers (2) ..	..		5·00	☐
		Presentation Pack (Nos. 1342/6)		4·00		☐
		PHQ Cards (set of 5) (Nos. 1342/6)		2·50	5·50	☐ ☐
		Set of 6 Gutter Pairs		8·00		☐

Collectors Pack 1986

1986 (18 Nov.) Comprises Nos. 1308/40, 1342/6

	Collectors Pack	30·00	☐

Post Office Yearbook

1986 Comprises Nos. 1308/40, 1342/6 in hardbound book with slip case.

	Yearbook	50·00	☐

819 North American Blanket Flower

820 Globe Thistle

821 Echeveria

822 Autumn Crocus

Flower Photographs by Alfred Lammer

1987 (20 Jan.) Phosphorised paper. Perf $14\frac{1}{2} \times 14$

1347	**819**	18p multicoloured		50	50	☐ ☐
1348	**820**	22p multicoloured		60	65	☐ ☐
1349	**821**	31p multicoloured		90	95	☐ ☐
1350	**822**	34p multicoloured		1·00	1·10	☐ ☐
		Set of 4		2·75	3·00	☐ ☐
		First Day Cover			3·75	☐
		Presentation Pack.. ..		3·50		☐
		PHQ Cards (set of 4) ..		2·00	5·75	☐ ☐
		Set of 4 Gutter Pairs ..		5·75		☐

823 The Principia Mathematica

824 Motion of Bodies in Ellipses

825 Optick Treatise

826 The System of the World

300th Anniversary of The Principia Mathematica by Sir Isaac Newton

1987 (24 Mar.) Phosphorised paper.

1351	**823**	18p multicoloured	..	50	50	☐ ☐
1352	**824**	22p multicoloured	..	60	65	☐ ☐
1353	**825**	31p multicoloured	..	90	95	☐ ☐
1354	**826**	34p multicoloured	..	1·00	1·10	☐ ☐
		Set of 4		2·75	3·00	☐ ☐
		First Day Cover			3·75	☐
		Presentation Pack.. ..		3·50		☐
		PHQ Cards (set of 4) ..		2·00	5·00	☐ ☐
		Set of 4 Gutter Pairs ..		5·75		☐

For full information on all future British issues, collectors should write to the British Post Office Philatelic Bureau, 20 Brandon Street, Edinburgh EH3 5TT

827 Willis Faber and Dumas Building, Ipswich

828 Pompidou Centre, Paris

829 Staatsgalerie, Stuttgart

830 European Investment Bank, Luxembourg

Europa. British Architects in Europe

1987 (12 MAY) *Phosphorised paper.*

1355	827	18p multicoloured	..	50	50	☐	☐
1356	828	22p multicoloured	..	60	65	☐	☐
1357	829	31p multicoloured	..	90	95	☐	☐
1358	830	34p multicoloured	..	1·00	1·10	☐	☐
		Set of 4	.. .. ..	2·75	3·00	☐	☐
		First Day Cover	.. ..		3·75	☐	
		Presentation Pack..	.. ..	3·50		☐	
		PHQ Cards (set of 4)	..	2·00	5·00	☐	☐
		Set of 4 Gutter Pairs	.. ..	5·75		☐	

831 Brigade Members with Ashford Litter, 1887

832 Bandaging Blitz Victim, 1940

833 Volunteer with fainting Girl, 1965

834 Transport of Transplant Organ by Air Wing, 1987

Centenary of St. John Ambulance Brigade

1987 (16 JUNE) *Phosphorised paper. Perf 14 × 14½*

1359	831	18p multicoloured	..	50	50	☐	
1360	832	22p multicoloured	..	60	65	☐	
1361	833	31p multicoloured	..	90	95	☐	
1362	834	34p multicoloured	..	1·00	1·10	☐	☐
		Set of 4	.. .. ..	2·75	3·00	☐	☐
		First Day Cover	..		3·75		☐
		Presentation Pack..	..	3·50		☐	
		PHQ Cards (set of 4)	..	2·00	5·00	☐	☐
		Set of 4 Gutter Pairs	.. ..	5·75		☐	

835 Arms of the Lord Lyon King of Arms

836 Scottish Heraldic Banner of Prince Charles

837 Arms of Royal Scottish Academy of Painting, Sculpture and Architecture

838 Arms of Royal Society of Edinburgh

300th Anniversary of Revival of Order of the Thistle

1987 (21 JULY) *Phosphorised paper. Perf 14½*

1363	835	18p multicoloured	..	50	50	☐	☐
1364	836	22p multicoloured	..	60	65	☐	☐
1365	837	31p multicoloured	..	90	95	☐	☐
1366	838	34p multicoloured	..	1·00	1·10	☐	☐
		Set of 4	.. .. ..	2·75	3·00		☐
		First Day Cover	..		3·75		☐
		Presentation Pack..	.. ..	3·50		☐	
		PHQ Cards (set of 4)	..	2·00	5·00	☐	☐
		Set of 4 Gutter Pairs	.. ..	5·75		☐	

839 Crystal Palace, 'Monarch of the Glen' (Landseer) and Grace Darling

840 Great Eastern, Beeton's Book of Household Management and Prince Albert

841 Albert Memorial, Ballot Box and Disraeli

842 Diamond Jubilee Emblem, Morse Key and Newspaper Placard for Relief of Mafeking

150th Anniversary of Queen Victoria's Accession

1987 (8 SEPT.) Phosphorised paper.

1367	839	18p multicoloured	..	50	50	□	□
1368	840	22p multicoloured	..	60	65	□	□
1369	841	31p multicoloured	..	90	95	□	□
1370	842	34p multicoloured	..	1·00	1·10	□	□
		Set of 4		2·75	3·00	□	□
		First Day Cover			3·75	□	
		Presentation Pack ..			3·50		□
		PHQ Cards (set of 4)		2·00	5·00	□	□
		Set of 4 Gutter Pairs		5·75			□

843 Pot by Bernard Leach

844 Pot by Elizabeth Fritsch

845 Pot by Lucie Rie

846 Pot by Hans Coper

Studio Pottery

1987 (13 OCT.) Phosphorised paper. Perf 14½ × 14

1371	843	18p multicoloured	..	50	50	□	□
1372	844	26p multicoloured	..	70	70	□	□
1373	845	31p multicoloured	..	1·00	95	□	□
1374	846	34p multicoloured	..	1·00	1·10	□	□
		Set of 4		3·00	3·00	□	□
		First Day Cover			4·00		□
		Presentation Pack		3·50			□
		PHQ Cards (set of 4)		2·00	5·00	□	□
		Set of 4 Gutter Pairs		6·00			□

Nos. 1371/4 also mark the birth centenary of Bernard Leach, the potter.

847 Decorating the Christmas tree

848 Waiting for Father Christmas

849 Sleeping Child and Father Christmas in Sleigh

850 Child reading

851 Child playing Flute and Snowman

Christmas

1987 (17 Nov.) One phosphor band (13p) or phosphorised paper (others)

1375	847	13p multicoloured	..	40	40	□	□
1376	848	18p multicoloured	..	50	50	□	□
1377	849	26p multicoloured	..	75	75	□	□
1378	850	31p multicoloured	..	90	90	□	□
1379	851	34p multicoloured	..	1·00	1·00	□	□
		Set of 5		3·25	3·25	□	□
		First Day Cover			4·00		□
		Presentation Pack		3·75			□
		PHQ Cards (set of 5)		2·25	5·75	□	□
		Set of 5 Gutter Pairs		6·50			□

Collectors Pack 1987

1987 (17 Nov.) *Comprises Nos. 1347/79*
    Collectors Pack .. .. .. 25·00 ☐

Post Office Yearbook

1987 *Comprises Nos. 1347/79 in hardbound book with slip case*
    Yearbook .. .. 38·00 ☐

852 Bull-rout (Jonathan Couch)

853 Yellow Waterlily (Major Joshua Swatkin)

854 Bewick's Swan (Edward Lear)

855 *Morchella esculenta* (James Sowerby)

Bicentenary of Linnean Society. Archive Illustrations

1988 (19 JAN.) *Phosphorised paper*

1380	852	18p multicoloured	..	45	45	☐	☐
1381	853	26p multicoloured	..	65	65	☐	☐
1382	854	31p multicoloured	..	80	80	☐	☐
1383	855	34p multicoloured	..	90	90	☐	☐
		Set of 4 ..	.. ..	2·60	2·60	☐	☐
		First Day Cover	.. ..		3·75	☐	
		Presentation Pack ..	..	3·25		☐	
		PHQ Cards (set of 4)	.. ..	2·00	5·00	☐	☐
		Set of 4 Gutter Pairs	.. ..	5·25		☐	

856 Revd William Morgan (Bible translator, 1588)

857 William Salesbury (New Testament translator, 1567)

858 Bishop Richard Davies (New Testament translator, 1567)

859 Bishop Richard Parry (editor of Revised Welsh Bible, 1620)

400th Anniversary of Welsh Bible

1988 (1 MAR.) *Phosphorised paper. Perf* $14\frac{1}{2} \times 14$

1384	856	18p multicoloured	..	45	45	☐	☐
1385	857	26p multicoloured	..	65	65	☐	☐
1386	858	31p multicoloured	..	80	80	☐	☐
1387	859	34p multicoloured	..	90	90	☐	☐
		Set of 4 ..	.. ..	2·60	2·60	☐	☐
		First Day Cover	.. ..		3·75		☐
		Presentation Pack ..	..	3·25		☐	
		PHQ Cards (set of 4)	.. ..	2·00	5·00	☐	☐
		Set of 4 Gutter Pairs	..	5·25		☐	

860 Gymnastics (Centenary of British Amateur Gymnastics Association)

861 Downhill Skiing (Ski Club of Great Britain)

862 Tennis (Centenary of Lawn Tennis Association)

863 Football (Centenary of Football League)

Sports Organizations

1988 (22 MAR.) Phosphorised paper. Perf 14½

388	860	18p multicoloured	..	45	45	☐	☐
389	861	26p multicoloured	..	65	65	☐	☐
390	862	31p multicoloured	..	80	80	☐	☐
391	863	34p multicoloured	..	90	90	☐	☐
		Set of 4		2·60	2·60	☐	☐
		First Day Cover			6·00		☐
		Presentation Pack		3·25		☐	
		PHQ Cards (set of 4) ..		2·00	5·00	☐	☐
		Set of 4 Gutter Pairs		5·25		☐	

864 *Mallard* and Mailbags on Pick-up Arms

865 Loading Transatlantic Mail on Liner *Queen Elizabeth*

866 Glasgow Tram No. 1173 and Pillar Box

867 Imperial Airways Handley Page "HP 24" and Airmail Van

Europa. Transport and Mail Services in 1930's

1988 (10 MAY) Phosphorised paper

392	864	18p multicoloured	..	50	50	☐	☐
393	865	26p multicoloured	..	60	65	☐	☐
394	866	31p multicoloured	..	90	1·00	☐	☐
395	867	34p multicoloured	..	1·00	1·00	☐	☐
		Set of 4		2·75	2·90	☐	☐
		First Day Cover			3·75		☐
		Presentation Pack		3·50		☐	
		PHQ Cards (set of 4) ..		2·00	5·00	☐	☐
		Set of 4 Gutter Pairs ..		5·50		☐	

868 Early Settler and Sailing Clipper

869 Queen Elizabeth II with British and Australian Parliament Buildings

870 W. G. Grace (cricketer) and Tennis Racquet

871 Shakespeare, John Lennon (entertainer) and Sydney Landmarks

Nos. 1396/7 and 1398/9 were each printed together, *se-tenant*, in horizontal pairs throughout the sheets, each pair showing a background design of the Australian flag.

Bicentenary of Australian Settlement

1988 (21 JUNE) Phosphorised paper. Perf 14½

1396	868	18p multicoloured	..	30	35	☐	☐
		a. Horiz. pair.					
		Nos. 1396/7 ..	..	75	80	☐	☐
1397	869	18p multicoloured	..	30	35	☐	☐
1398	870	34p multicoloured	..	80	1·00	☐	☐
		a. Horiz. pair.					
		Nos. 1398/9 ..	..	2·00	2·25	☐	☐
1399	871	34p multicoloured	..	80	1·00	☐	☐
		Set of 4	..	2·50	2·50	☐	☐
		First Day Cover			3·50		☐
		Presentation Pack		2·75		☐	
		Souvenir Book		6·00		☐	
		PHQ Cards (set of 4)		90	5·00	☐	☐
		Set of 4 Gutter Pairs		5·00		☐	

Stamps in similar designs were also issued by Australia.

872 Spanish Galeasse off The Lizard

873 English Fleet leaving Plymouth

874 Engagement off Isle of Wight

875 Attack of English Fire-ships, Calais

876 Armada in Storm,
North Sea

Nos. 1400/4 were each printed together, *se-tenant*, in horizontal strips of 5 throughout the sheet, forming a composite design.

400th Anniversary of Spanish Armada

1988 (19 JULY) *Phosphorised paper*

1400	**872**	18p multicoloured	..	40	40	☐	☐
		a. *Horiz strip* of 5.					
		Nos. 1400/4 ..	..	2·25	2·25	☐	☐
1401	**873**	18p multicoloured	..	40	40	☐	☐
1402	**874**	18p multicoloured	..	40	40	☐	☐
1403	**875**	18p multicoloured	..	40	40	☐	☐
1404	**876**	18p multicoloured	..	40	40	☐	☐
		Set of 5	..	2·25	1·75	☐	☐
		First Day Cover			3·25		☐
		Presentation Pack		2·50		☐	
		PHQ Cards (set of 5)		1·10	4·75	☐	☐
		Gutter strip of 10		4·50		☐	

877 "The Owl and the Pussy-cat"

878 "Edward Lear as a Bird" (self-portrait)

879 "Cat" (from alphabet book)

880 "There was a Young Lady whose Bonnet . . ." (limerick)

Death Centenary of Edward Lear (artist and author)

1988 (6–27 SEPT.) *Phosphorised paper*

1405	**877**	19p black, pale cream and carmine	40	40	☐	☐
1406	**878**	27p black, pale cream and yellow	55	55	☐	☐
1407	**879**	32p black, pale cream and emerald	75	75	☐	☐
1408	**880**	35p black, pale cream and blue	80	80	☐	☐
		Set of 4	2·25	2·25	☐	☐
		First Day Cover		3·75		☐
		Presentation Pack	2·50		☐	
		PHQ Cards (set of 4)	90	5·00	☐	☐
		Set of 4 Gutter Pairs ..	4·50		☐	
MS1409		122×90 mm. Nos. 1405/8	3·00	3·00	☐	☐
		First Day Cover (27 Sept.) ..		4·25		☐

No. **MS**1409 was sold at £1·35, the premium being used for the "Stamp World London 90" International Stamp Exhibition.

881 Carrickfergus Castle

882 Caernarvon Castle

883 Edinburgh Castle

884 Windsor Castle

1988 (18 OCT.) *Ordinary paper*

1410	**881**	£1 deep green	..	..	1·50	1·60	☐	☐
1411	**882**	£1·50 maroon	..	..	2·25	2·40	☐	☐
1412	**883**	£2 steel blue	..	..	3·00	3·25	☐	☐
1413	**884**.	£5 deep brown	..	..	7·50	7·75	☐	☐
		Set of 4	..	..	13·00	13·50	☐	☐
		First Day Cover ..	..			30·00		☐
		Presentation Pack ..	..		14·00		☐	
		Set of 4 Gutter Pairs	..	..	27·00		☐	

85 Journey to Bethlehem

886 Shepherds and Star

87 Three Wise Men

888 Nativity

889 The Annunciation

890 Puffin

891 Avocet

892 Oystercatcher

893 Gannet

Christmas

988 (15 Nov.) *One phosphor band (14p) or phosphorised paper (others)*

114	**885**	14p multicoloured	..		35	30	□ □
115	**886**	19p multicoloured	..		40	35	□ □
116	**887**	27p multicoloured	..		60	60	□ □
117	**888**	32p multicoloured	..		70	75	□ □
118	**889**	35p multicoloured	..		75	80	□ □
		Set of 5 ..	..	..	2·50	2·50	□ □
		First Day Cover	..	..		4·00	□
		Presentation Pack	..		2·75		□
		PHQ Cards (set of 5)	..		1·10	5·25	□ □
		Set of 5 Gutter Pairs	..		5·00		□

Collectors Pack 1988

988 (15 Nov.) *Comprises Nos. 1380/1408, 1414/18*

	Collectors Pack	..	..	25·00 □

Post Office Yearbook

988 *Comprises Nos. 1380/1404. MS1409, 1414/18 in hardbound book with slip case*

	Yearbook	..	..	38·00 □

Centenary of Royal Society for the Protection of Birds

1989 (17 Jan.) *Phosphorised paper*

1419	**890**	19p multicoloured	..	30	35	□ □
1420	**891**	27p multicoloured	..	45	50	□ □
1421	**892**	32p multicoloured	..	50	55	□ □
1422	**893**	35p multicoloured	..	55	60	□ □
		Set of 4	..	1·60	1·75	□ □
		First Day Cover			3·00	□
		Presentation Pack		2·00		□
		PHQ Cards (set of 4)		90	4·50	□ □
		Set of 4 Gutter Pairs		3·50		□

894 Rose

895 Cupid

896 Yachts

897 Fruit

898 Teddy Bear

903 Mortar Board (150th Anniv. of Public Education in England)

904 Cross on Ballot Paper (3rd Direct Elections to European Parliament)

Greetings Booklet Stamps

1989 (31 Jan.) *Phosphorised paper*

1423	**894**	19p multicoloured	..	30	35 ☐ ☐
		a. *Booklet pane.*			
		Nos. 1423/7 × 2	..	3·00	☐
1424	**895**	19p multicoloured	..	30	35 ☐ ☐
1425	**896**	19p multicoloured	..	30	35 ☐ ☐
1426	**897**	19p multicoloured	..	30	35 ☐ ☐
1427	**898**	19p multicoloured	..	30	35 ☐ ☐
		Set of 5	..	1·40	1·60 ☐ ☐
		First Day Cover			3·25 ☐

905 Posthorn (26th Postal, Telegraph and Telephone International Congress Brighton)

906 Globe (Inter-Parliamentary Union Centenary Conference, London)

899 Fruit and Vegetables

900 Meat Products

901 Dairy Produce

902 Cereal Products

Anniversaries

1989 (11 Apr.) *Phosphorised paper. Perf* $14 \times 14\frac{1}{2}$

1432	**903**	19p multicoloured	..	30	35 ☐
		a. *Horiz pair.*			
		Nos. 1432/3	..	60	70 ☐
1433	**904**	19p multicoloured	..	30	35 ☐
1434	**905**	35p multicoloured	..	55	60 ☐
		a. *Horiz pair.*			
		Nos. 1434/5	..	1·10	1·25 ☐
1435	**906**	35p multicoloured	..	55	60 ☐
		Set of 4	..	1·50	1·75 ☐
		First Day Cover	..		3·25
		Presentation Pack ..	..	2·00	☐
		PHQ Cards (set of 4)	..	90	4·50 ☐
		Set of 2 Gutter Pairs	..	1·75	☐

Food and Farming Year

1989 (7 Mar.) *Phosphorised paper. Perf* $14 \times 14\frac{1}{2}$

1428	**899**	19p multicoloured	..	30	35 ☐ ☐
1429	**900**	27p multicoloured	..	45	50 ☐ ☐
1430	**901**	32p multicoloured	..	50	55 ☐ ☐
1431	**902**	35p multicoloured	..	55	60 ☐ ☐
		Set of 4	..	1·60	1·75 ☐ ☐
		First Day Cover			3·25 ☐
		Presentation Pack ..	..	2·00	☐
		PHQ Cards (set of 4)	..	90	4·50 ☐ ☐
		Set of 4 Gutter Pairs	..	3·50	☐

907 Toy Train and Airplane

908 Building Bricks

Dice and Board Games

910 Toy Robot, Boat and Doll's House

opa. Games and Toys

9 (16 MAY) *Phosphorised paper*

6	**907**	19p multicoloured	..	30	35	□ □
7	**908**	27p multicoloured	..	45	50	□ □
8	**909**	32p multicoloured	..	50	55	□ □
9	**910**	35p multicoloured	..	55	60	□ □
		Set of 4	..	1·60	1·75	□ □
		First Day Cover			3·25	□
		Presentation Pack	..	2·00		□
		PHQ Cards (set of 4) ..	..	90	4·50	□ □
		Set of 4 Gutter Pairs ..	..	3·50		□

Ironbridge, Shropshire

912 Tin Mine, St. Agnes Head, Cornwall

Cotton Mills, New Lanark, Strathclyde

914 Pontcysyllte Aqueduct, Clwyd

915

Industrial Archaeology

1989 (4–25 JULY) *Phosphorised paper*

1440	**911**	19p multicoloured	..	30	35	□ □
1441	**912**	27p multicoloured	..	45	50	□ □
1442	**913**	32p multicoloured	..	50	55	□ □
1443	**914**	35p multicoloured	..	55	60	□ □
		Set of 4	..	1·60	1·75	□ □
		First Day Cover			3·25	□
		Presentation Pack	..	2·00		□
		PHQ Cards (set of 4) ..	..	90	4·50	□ □
		Set of 4 Gutter Pairs ..	..	3·50		□
MS1444		122 × 90 mm. **915** As Nos.				
		1440/3 but designs horizontal	..	2·10	2·25	□ □
		First Day Cover (25 July) ..			3·50	□

No. **MS**1444 was sold at £1.40, the premium being used for the "Stamp World London 90" International Stamp Exhibition.

916

917

Booklet Stamps

1989 (22 AUG. – 19 SEPT.)

(a) Printed in photogravure by Harrison and Sons. Perf 15 × 14

1445	**916**	(2nd) bright blue (1 centre band)	25	30	□ □
1446	**917**	(1st) black (phosphorised paper)	30	35	□ □

(b) Printed in lithography by Walsall. Perf 14

1447	**916**	(2nd) bright blue (1 centre band)	25	30	□ □
1448	**917**	(1st) black (2 bands) ..	30	35	□ □

(c) Printed in lithography by Questa Perf 15 × 14 (19 Sept)

1449	**916**	(2nd) bright blue (1 centre band)	25	30	□ □
1450	**917**	(1st) black (phosphorised paper)	30	35	□ □

918 Snowflake (× 10)

919 Blue Fly (× 5)

924 Lord Mayor's Coach

925 Coach Team passing St Pa

920 Blood Cells (× 500)

921 Microchip (× 600)

926 Blues and Royals Drum Horse

150th Anniversary of Royal Microscopical Society

1989 (5 Sept.) *Phosphorised paper. Perf* $14\frac{1}{2} \times 14$

1451	**918**	19p multicoloured	..	30	35	□	□
1452	**919**	27p multicoloured	..	45	50	□	□
1453	**920**	32p multicoloured	..	50	55	□	□
1454	**921**	35p multicoloured	..	55	60	□	□
		Set of 4	.. .. ..	1·60	1·75	□	□
		First Day Cover	.. ..		3·25		□
		Presentation Pack	.. .. ..	2·00		□	
		PHQ Cards (set of 4)	.. ..	90	4·50	□	□
		Set of 4 Gutter Pairs	.. ..	3·50		□	

Lord Mayor's Show, London

1989 (17 Oct.) *Phosphorised paper*

1455	**922**	20p multicoloured	..	30	35	□
		a. Horiz strip of 5.				
		Nos. 1455/9	..	1·40	1·50	□
1456	**923**	20p multicoloured	..	30	35	□
1457	**924**	20p multicoloured	..	30	35	□
1458	**925**	20p multicoloured	..	30	35	□
1459	**926**	20p multicoloured	..	30	35	□
		Set of 5	.. .. ..	1·40	1·50	□
		First Day Cover	.. ..		2·25	□
		Presentation Pack	.. ..	1·90		□
		PHQ Cards (set of 5)	.. ..	1·40	3·75	□
		Gutter Strip of 10	.. ..	3·00		□

Nos. 1455/9 commemorate the 800th anniversary of installation of the first Lord Mayor of London.

922 Royal Mail Coach

923 Escort of Blues and Royals

927 14th-century Peasants from Stained-glass Window

928 Arches and Roundels, West Front

89

929 Octagon Tower

930 Arcade from West Transept

931 Triple Arch from West Front

Christmas. 800th Anniversary of Ely Cathedral

1989 (14 Nov.) *One phosphor band (Nos. 1460/1) or phosphorised paper (others)*

1460	**927**	15p gold, silver and blue	25	30	□ □
1461	**928**	15p + 1p gold, silver and blue	25	30	□ □
1462	**929**	20p + 1p gold, silver and rosine	35	40	□ □
1463	**930**	34p + 1p gold, silver and emerald	55	60	□ □
1464	**931**	37p + 1p gold, silver and yellow-olive	60	65	□ □
		Set of 5	1·75	2·00	□ □
		First Day Cover		2·75	□
		Presentation Pack	2·25		□
		PHQ Cards (set of 5)	1·40	4·25	□ □
		Set of 5 Gutter Pairs	3·50		□

Collectors Pack 1989

1989 (14 Nov.) *Comprises Nos. 1419/22, 1428/43 and 1451/4*

Collectors Pack	.. .. ..	14·50	□

Post Office Yearbook

1989 *Comprises Nos. 1419/22, 1428/44 and 1451/4 in hardback book with slip case.*

Yearbook	.. .. ..	26·00	□

REGIONAL ISSUES

PERFORATION AND WATERMARK. All the following Regional stamps are perforated 15×14 and are watermarked Type **179**, unless otherwise stated.

For listing of First Day Covers see pages 97/8.

1 Northern Ireland

| N 1 | N 2 | N 3 | N 4 |

1958–67

NI1	N 1	3d	lilac		10	10	☐ ☐
		p.	One centre phosphor band		10	15	☐ ☐
NI2		4d	blue		10	12	☐ ☐
		p.	Two phosphor bands		10	15	☐ ☐
NI3	N 2	6d	purple		20	20	☐ ☐
NI4		9d	bronze-green (2 phosphor bands)		30	50	☐ ☐
NI5	N 3	1s 3d	green		30	50	☐ ☐
NI6		1s 6d	blue (2 phosphor bands)		30	50	☐ ☐

1968–70 *One centre phosphor band (Nos. N18/9) or two phosphor bands (others). No wmk*

NI7	N 1	4d	blue		10	12	☐ ☐
NI8		4d	sepia		10	12	☐ ☐
NI9		4d	vermilion		20	20	☐ ☐
NI10		5d	blue		12	20	☐ ☐
NI11	N 3	1s 6d	blue		2·50	3·00	☐ ☐
		Presentation Pack (comprises Nos. NI1p, NI4/6, NI8/10)			3·00		☐

Decimal Currency

1971–88 *Type N 4 No wmk*

(a) Printed in photogravure with phosphor bands

NI12	2½p	magenta (1 centre band)		90	25	☐ ☐
NI13	3p	ultramarine (2 bands)		40	15	☐ ☐
NI14	3p	ultramarine (1 centre band)		15	15	☐ ☐
NI15	3½p	olive-grey (2 bands)		20	20	☐ ☐
NI16	3½p	olive-grey (1 centre band)		20	25	☐ ☐
NI17	4½p	grey-blue (2 bands)		25	25	☐ ☐
NI18	5p	violet (2 bands)		1·50	1·50	☐ ☐
NI19	5½p	violet (2 bands)		20	20	☐ ☐
NI20	5½p	violet (1 centre band)		20	20	☐ ☐
NI21	6½p	blue (1 centre band)		20	20	☐ ☐
NI22	7p	brown (1 centre band)		25	25	☐ ☐
NI23	7½p	chestnut (2 bands)		2·50	2·50	☐ ☐
NI24	8p	rosine (2 bands)		30	30	☐ ☐
NI25	8½p	yellow-green (2 bands)		30	30	☐ ☐
NI26	9p	violet (2 bands)		30	30	☐ ☐
NI27	10p	orange-brown (2 bands)		35	35	☐ ☐
NI28	10p	orange-brown (1 centre band)		35	35	☐ ☐
NI29	10½p	blue (2 bands)		40	40	☐ ☐
NI30	11p	scarlet (2 bands)		40	40	☐ ☐

(b) Printed in photogravure on phosphorised paper

NI31	12p	yellowish green		40	45	☐ ☐
NI32	13½p	purple-brown		60	70	☐ ☐
NI33	15p	ultramarine		45	50	☐ ☐

(c) Printed in lithography with one side phosphor band (11½p, 12p, 12½p, 13p, 14p (No. NI39) or on phosphorised paper (others). Perf 13½×14 (11½p, 12½p, 14p (No. NI38), 15½p, 16p, 18p (No. NI43), 19½p, 20½p, 22p (No. NI48), 26p, 28p) or 15×14 (others)

NI34	11½p	drab		80	60	☐ ☐
NI35	12p	bright emerald		50	50	☐ ☐
NI36	12½p	light emerald		50	40	☐ ☐
		a Perf 15×14		4·00	4·00	☐ ☐
NI37	13p	pale chestnut		20	35	☐ ☐
NI38	14p	grey-blue		60	50	☐ ☐
NI39	14p	deep blue		25	30	☐ ☐
NI40	15½p	pale violet		60	65	☐ ☐
NI41	16p	drab		1·10	1·00	☐ ☐
		a Perf 15×14		3·00	1·00	☐ ☐
NI42	17p	grey-blue		60	40	☐ ☐
NI43	18p	deep violet		80	80	☐ ☐
NI44	18p	olive-grey		30	45	☐ ☐
NI45	19p	bright orange-red		30	35	☐ ☐
NI46	19½p	olive-grey		2·00	2·00	☐ ☐
NI47	20½p	ultramarine		1·50	1·50	☐ ☐
NI48	22p	blue		80	1·10	☐ ☐
NI49	22p	yellow-green		35	50	☐ ☐
NI50	23p	bright green		35	40	☐ ☐
NI51	26p	rosine		80	80	☐ ☐
		a Perf 15×14		40	60	☐ ☐
NI52	28p	deep violet-blue		85	80	☐ ☐
		a Perf 15×14		45	65	☐ ☐
NI53	31p	bright purple		50	80	☐ ☐
NI54	32p	greenish blue		50	60	☐ ☐

Presentation Pack (contains 2½p (NI12), 3p (NI13), 5p (NI18), 7½p (NI23))	4·00	☐
Presentation Pack (contains 3p (NI14), 3½p (NI15), 5½p (NI19), 8p (NI24) later with 4½p (NI17) added)	3·00	☐
Presentation Pack (contains 6½p (NI21), 8½p (NI25), 10p (NI27), 11p (NI30))	1·75	☐
Presentation Pack (contains 7p (NI22), 9p (NI26), 10½p (NI29), 11½p (NI34), 12p (NI31), 13½p (NI32), 14p (NI38), 15p (NI33), 18p (N143), 22p (NI48))	6·00	☐

Presentation Pack (contains
10p (NI28), 12½p (NI36),
16p (NI41), 20½p (NI47),
26p (N151), 28p (N152)) ..   5·00 ☐

Presentation Pack (contains
10p (NI28), 13p (NI37),
16p (NI41a), 17p (NI42),
22p (NI49), 26p (NI51),
28p (NI52), 31p (NI53)) ..   8·00 ☐

Presentation Pack (contains
12p (NI35), 13p (NI37),
17p (NI42), 20½p (NI44),
22p (NI49), 26p (NI51a),
28p (NI52a), 31p (NI53)) ..   3·00 ☐

Presentation Pack (contains
14p, 19p, 23p, 32p from
Northern Ireland, Scotland
and Wales (Nos. NI39, NI45,
NI50, NI54, S54, S58, S61,
S66, W40, W46, W51, W55))   4·25 ☐

2 Scotland

S 1   S 2   S 3   S 4

1958–67

S1	S 1	3d lilac		10	12	☐ ☐
		p. Two phosphor bands		15·00	1·00	☐ ☐
		pa. One side band		20	25	☐ ☐
		pb. One centre band		10	12	☐ ☐
S2		4d blue		10	10	☐ ☐
		p. Two phosphor bands		10	20	☐ ☐
S3	S 2	6d purple		12	12	☐ ☐
		p. Two phosphor bands		15	25	☐ ☐
S4		9d bronze-green (2 phosphor bands)		30	30	☐ ☐
S5	S 3	1s 3d green		30	30	☐ ☐
		p. Two phosphor bands		30	30	☐ ☐
S6		1s 6d blue (2 phosphor bands)		35	30	☐ ☐

No. S1pa exists with the phosphor band at the left or right
of the stamp.

1967–70 One centre phosphor band (Nos. S7, S9/10) or two
phosphor bands (others). No wmk

S7	S 1	3d lilac		10	12	☐ ☐
S8		4d blue		10	12	☐ ☐
S9		4d sepia		10	10	☐ ☐
S10		4d vermilion		10	10	☐ ☐
S11		5d blue		20	10	☐ ☐
S12	S 2	9d bronze-green		5·50	5·50	☐ ☐
S13	S 3	1s 6d blue		1·40	1·00	☐ ☐
		Presentation Pack (containing Nos. S3, S5p, S7, S9/13)		13·00		☐

Decimal Currency

1971–88 Type S 4. No wmk

(a) Printed in photogravure by Harrison and Sons with phosphor bands. Perf 15 × 14.

S14	2½p magenta (1 centre band)		20	12	☐ ☐
S15	3p ultramarine (2 bands)		30	15	☐ ☐
S16	3p ultramarine (1 centre band)		15	12	☐ ☐
S17	3½p olive-grey (2 bands)		20	20	☐ ☐
S18	3½p ol-grey (1 centre band)		20	20	☐ ☐
S19	4½p grey-blue (2 bands)		25	20	☐ ☐
S20	5p violet (2 bands)		1·50	1·50	☐ ☐
S21	5½p violet (2 bands)		20	20	☐ ☐
S22	5½p violet (1 centre band)		20	20	☐ ☐
S23	6½p blue (1 centre band)		20	20	☐ ☐

24	7p	brown (1 centre band)	25	25	☐	☐
25	7½p	chestnut (2 bands) ..	2·00	2·00	☐	☐
26	8p	rosine (2 bands)	30	40	☐	☐
27	8½p	yellow-green (2 bands)	30	30	☐	☐
28	9p	violet (2 bands) ..	30	30	☐	☐
29	10p	orange-brown (2 bands)	35	30	☐	☐
30	10p	orange-brown (1 centre band)	35	35	☐	☐
31	10½p	blue (2 bands) ..	40	35	☐	☐
32	11p	scarlet (2 bands) ..	40	35	☐	☐

) Printed in photogravure by Harrison and Sons on phosphorised paper. Perf 15 × 14

33	12p	yellowish green ..	40	30	☐	☐
34	13½p	purple-brown	60	65	☐	☐
35	15p	ultramarine ..	45	45	☐	☐

) Printed in lithography by John Waddington. One side Phosphor band (11½p, 12p, 12½p, 13p) or phosphorised paper (others). Perf 13½ × 14

36	11½p	drab	75	60	☐	☐
37	12p	bright emerald	55	70	☐	☐
38	12½p	light emerald	40	40	☐	☐
39	13p	pale chestnut	40	30	☐	☐
40	14p	grey-blue	55	50	☐	☐
41	15½p	pale violet	60	65	☐	☐
42	16p	drab	55	45	☐	☐
43	17p	grey-blue	3·00	2·00	☐	☐
44	18p	deep violet	70	65	☐	☐
45	19½p	olive-grey	2·00	2·25	☐	☐
46	20½p	ultramarine	1·50	1·50	☐	☐
47	22p	blue	80	1·10	☐	☐
48	22p	yellow-green	80	80	☐	☐
49	26p	rosine	80	80	☐	☐
50	28p	deep violet-blue ..	85	80	☐	☐
51	31p	bright purple	80	90	☐	☐

(d) Printed in lithography by Questa. Perf 15 × 14

52	12p	brt emer (1 side band) ..	50	60	☐	☐
53	13p	pale chest (1 side band)	20	30	☐	☐
54	14p	dp bl (1 centre band) ..	25	30	☐	☐
55	14p	deep blue (1 side band)	30	35	☐	☐
56	17p	grey-bl (phosphorised paper)	3·00	2·00	☐	☐
57	18p	ol-grey (phosphorised paper)	30	45	☐	☐
58	19p	bright orange-red (phosphorised paper) ..	30	35	☐	☐
59	19p	brt orge-red (2 bands) ..	40	45	☐	☐
60	22p	yell-grn (phosphorised paper)	35	50	☐	☐
61	23p	brt grn (phosphorised paper)	35	40	☐	☐
62	23p	bright green (2 bands)	65	70	☐	☐
63	26p	rosine (phosphorised paper)	40	60	☐	☐
4	28p	deep violet-blue (phosphorised paper) ..	45	65	☐	☐
5	31p	bright purple (phosphorised paper) ..	50	70	☐	☐
6	32p	greenish blue (phosphorised paper) ..	50	60	☐	☐

Presentation Pack (contains 2½p (S14), 3p (S15), 5p (S20), 7½p (S25))	4·00	☐
Presentation Pack (contains 3p (S16), 3½p (S17), 5½p (S21), 8p (S26) later with 4½p (S19) added)	3·00	☐
Presentation Pack (contains 6½p (S23), 8½p (S27), 10p (S29), 11p (S32))	1·75	☐
Presentation Pack (contains 7p (S24), 9p (S28), 10½p (S31), 11½p (S36), 12p (S33), 13½p (S34), 14p (S40), 15p (S35), 18p (S44), 22p (S47)) ..	6·00	☐
Presentation Pack (contains 10p (S30), 12½p (S38), 16p (S42), 20½p (S46), 26p (S49), 28p (S50))	5·00	☐
Presentation Pack (contains 10p (S30), 13p (S39), 16p (S42), 17p (S43), 22p (S48), 26p (S49), 28p (S50), 31p (S51))	8·00	☐
Presentation Pack (contains 12p (S52), 13p (S53), 17p (S56), 18p (S57), 22p (S60), 26p (S63), 28p (S64), 31p (S65)	3·00	☐

For combined pack containing 14p, 19p, 23p and 32p values from all three Regions see under Northern Ireland.

3 Wales and Monmouthshire

W 1    W 2    W 3    W 4

1958–67

W1	W 1	3d lilac	10	10	☐	☐
		p. One centre phosphor band	10	15	☐	☐
W2		4d blue	10	12	☐	☐
		p. Two phosphor bands	10	12	☐	☐
W3	W 2	6d purple	40	20	☐	☐
W4		9d bronze-green (2 phosphor bands)	30	35	☐	☐
W5	W 3	1s 3d green	30	30	☐	☐
W6		1s 6d blue (2 phosphor bands)	35	30	☐	☐

1967–70 One centre phosphor band (Nos. W7, W9/10) or two phosphor bands (others). No wmk

W7	W 1	3d lilac	10	10	☐	☐
W8		4d blue	10	10	☐	☐
W9		4d sepia	10	10	☐	☐
W10		4d vermilion	12	20	☐	☐
W11		5d blue	12	10	☐	☐
W12	W 3	1s 6d blue	3·00	3·00	☐	☐
		Presentation Pack (comprises Nos. W4, W6/7, W9/11)	2·50		☐	

Decimal Currency

1971–88 Type W 4. No wmk

(a) Printed in photogravure with phosphor bands

W13	2½p magenta (1 centre band)		15	12	☐	☐
W14	3p ultramarine (2 bands)		25	12	☐	☐
W15	3p ultramarine (1 centre band)		15	20	☐	☐
W16	3½p olive-grey (2 bands)		20	25	☐	☐
W17	3½p olive-grey (1 centre band)		20	25	☐	☐
W18	4½p grey-blue (2 bands)		25	20	☐	☐
W19	5p violet (2 bands)		1·50	1·50	☐	☐
W20	5½p violet (2 bands)		20	25	☐	☐
W21	5½p violet (1 centre band)		20	25	☐	☐
W22	6½p blue (1 centre band)		20	20	☐	☐
W23	7p brown (1 centre band)		25	25	☐	☐
W24	7½p chestnut (2 bands)		2·00	2·25	☐	☐
W25	8p rosine (2 bands)		30	30	☐	☐
W26	8½p yellow-green (2 bands)		30	30	☐	☐
W27	9p violet (2 bands)		30	30	☐	☐
W28	10p orange-brown (2 bands)		35	30	☐	☐
W29	10p orange-brown (1 centre band)		35	30	☐	☐
W30	10½p blue (2 bands)		40	35	☐	☐
W31	11p scarlet (2 bands)		40	45	☐	☐

(b) Printed in photogravure on phosphorised paper

W32	12p yellowish green		40	45	☐	☐
W33	13½p purple-brown		60	70	☐	☐
W34	15p ultramarine		45	50	☐	☐

(c) Printed in lithography with one side phosphor band (11½p, 12p, 12½p, 13p, 14p (No. W40)) or on phosphorised paper (others). Perf 13½×14 (11½p, 12½p, 14p (No. W39), 15½p, 16p, 18p (No. W44), 19½p, 20½p, 22p (No. W49)), 26p, 28p) or 15×14 (others)

W35	11½p drab		75	60	☐	☐
W36	12p bright emerald		50	50	☐	☐
W37	12½p light emerald		40	45	☐	☐
	a Perf 15×14		4·50	3·75	☐	☐
W38	13p pale chestnut		20	35	☐	☐
W39	14p grey-blue		55	50	☐	☐
W40	14p deep blue		25	30	☐	☐
W41	15½p pale violet		60	65	☐	☐
W42	16p drab		1·00	1·00	☐	☐
	a Perf 15×14		80	1·00	☐	☐
W43	17p grey-blue		60	45	☐	☐
W44	18p deep violet		70	75	☐	☐
W45	18p olive-grey		30	45	☐	☐
W46	19p bright orange-red		30	35	☐	☐
W47	19½p olive-grey		1·90	2·00	☐	☐
W48	20½p ultramarine		1·50	1·50	☐	☐
W49	22p blue		80	1·10	☐	☐
W50	22p yellow-green		35	50	☐	☐
W51	23p bright green		35	40	☐	☐
W52	26p rosine		80	80	☐	☐
	a Perf 15×14		40	60	☐	☐
W53	28p deep violet-blue		85	80	☐	☐
	a Perf 15×14		45	65	☐	☐
W54	31p bright purple		50	70	☐	☐
W55	32p greenish blue		55	60	☐	☐

Presentation Pack (contains 2½p (W13), 3p (W14), 5p (W19), 7½p (W24))	4·00	☐
Presentation Pack (contains 3p (W15), 3½p (W16), 5½p (W20), 8p (W25), later with 4½p (W18) added)	3·00	☐
Presentation Pack (contains 6½p (W22), 8½p (W26), 10p (W28), 11p (W31))	1·75	☐
Presentation Pack (contains 7p (W23), 9p (W27), 10½p (W30), 11½p (W35), 12p (W32), 13½p (W33), 14p (W39), 15p (W34), 18p (W44), 22p (W49))	6·00	☐
Presentation Pack (contains 10p (W29), 12½p (W37), 16p (W42), 20½p (W48), 26p (W52), 28p (W53))	5·00	

*Presentation Pack (contains
10p (W29), 13p (W38), 16p
(W42a), 17p (W43), 22p
(W50), 26p (W52), 28p
(W53), 31p (W54))* .. .. 8·50 ☐

*Presentation Pack (contains
12p (W36), 13p (W38), 17p
(W43), 18p (W45), 22p
(W50), 26p (W52a), 28p
(W53a), 31p (W54))* .. .. 3·00 ☐

For combined pack containing 14p, 19p, 23p and 32p
alues from all three Regions see under Northern Ireland.

ISLE OF MAN

Regional Issues

1   2   3

1958–67 *Wmk* **179** *Perf* 15×14

1	1	2½d red	45	80	☐	☐
2	2	3d lilac	10	10	☐	☐
		p. One centre phosphor band	10	30	☐	☐
3		4d blue	1·50	1·10	☐	☐
		p. Two phosphor bands	12	12	☐	☐

1968–69 *One centre phosphor band (Nos. 5/6) or two
phosphor bands (others). No wmk*

4	2	4d blue	10	25	☐	☐
5		4d sepia	10	30	☐	☐
6		4d vermilion ..	45	60	☐	☐
7		5d blue	45	60	☐	☐

Decimal Currency

1971 (7 JULY) *One centre phosphor band (2½p) or two
phosphor bands (others). No wmk*

8	3	2½p magenta	12	15	☐	☐
9		3p ultramarine ..	15	15	☐	☐
10		5p violet	70	75	☐	☐
11		7½p chestnut	70	90	☐	☐
		Presentation Pack	2·00		☐	

For comprehensive listings of the Independent Administration
issues of the Isle of Man, see Stanley Gibbons *Collect Channel
Islands and Isle of Man Stamps.*

CHANNEL ISLANDS

1 General Issue

C 1 Gathering Vraic   C 2 Islanders gathering Vraic

Third Anniversary of Liberation

1948 (10 MAY) *Wmk Type* **127** *Perf* 15×14

Cl	C 1	1d red	10	10	☐	☐
C2	C 2	2½d blue	15	15	☐	☐
		First Day Cover	15·00		☐	

2 Guernsey

(a) War Occupation Issues

Stamps issued under British authority during the German Occupation.

1   2   3

1941–44 *Rouletted.* (a) *White paper. No wmk*

1	1	½d green	..	..	2·50	2·50	□ □
2		1d red ..	..	..	1·50	1·25	□ □
3a		2½d blue	..	..	5·50	4·50	□ □

(b) *Bluish French bank-note paper. Wmk loops*

4	1	½d green	..	..	12·00	22·00	□ □
5		1d red ..	..	..	8·00	22·00	□ □

(b) Regional Issues

1958–67 *Wmk* 179   *Perf* 15 × 14

6	2	2½d red ..	..	..	35	40	□ □
7	3	3d lilac	..	..	35	30	□ □
		p. One centre phosphor band			12	20	□ □
8		4d blue	..	..	25	30	□ □
		p. Two phosphor bands	..	..	10	20	□ □

1968–69 *One centre phosphor band (Nos. 10/11) or two phosphor bands (others). No wmk*

9	3	4d blue	..	..	10	25	□ □
10		4d sepia	..	..	12	20	□ □
11		4d vermilion	..	..	12	30	□ □
12		5d blue	..	..	12	30	□ □

For comprehensive listings of the Independent Postal Administration issues of Guernsey, see Stanley Gibbons *Collect Channel Islands and Isle of Man Stamps.*

3 Jersey

(a) War Occupation Issues

Stamps issued under British authority during the German Occupation.

1   2 Old Jersey Farm   3 Portelet Bay

4 Corbière Lighthouse   5 Elizabeth Castle

6 Mont Orgueil Castle   7 Gathering Vraic (seaweed)

1941–42 *White paper. No wmk*   *Perf* 11

1	1	½d green	..	..	3·75	2·50	□ □
2		1d red ..	..	..	4·00	3·50	□ □

1943 *No wmk*   *Perf* 13½

3	2	½d green	..	..	7·00	3·75	□ □
4	3	1d red ..	..	..	1·00	50	□ □
5	4	1½d brown	..	..	2·00	3·00	□ □
6	5	2d orange	..	..	3·00	2·25	□ □
7a	6	2½d blue	..	..	75	2·00	□ □
8	7	3d violet	..	..	1·00	4·00	□ □
		Set of 6	..	..	13·00	14·00	□ □

(b) Regional Issues

8   9

1958–67 *Wmk* 179   *Perf* 15 × 14

9	8	2½d red ..	..	..	35	50	□
10	9	3d lilac	..	..	35	30	□
		p. One centre phospnor band			12	20	□
11		4d blue	..	..	25	30	□
		p. Two phosphor bands	..	..	10	25	□

1968–69 *One centre phosphor band (4d values) or tw phosphor bands (5d). No wmk*

12	9	4d sepia	..	..	12	25	□
13		4d vermilion	..	..	12	30	□
14		5d blue	..	..	12	30	□

For comprehensive listings of the Independent Post Administration issues of Jersey, see Stanley Gibbons *Colle Channel Islands and Isle of Man Stamps.*

ICES for First Day Covers listed below are for stamps, as
icated, used on illustrated envelopes and postmarked with
rational cancellations (before 1964) or with special First
y of Issue cancellations (1964 onwards). First Day
tmarks of 8 June 1964 and 7 February 1966 were of the
chine cancellation "envelope" type.

d Issues

Aug. 1958	Guernsey 3d (*No. 7*)	7·50	☐
	Isle of Man 3d (*No. 2*)	13·00	☐
	Jersey 3d (*No. 10*)	10·00	☐
	Northern Ireland 3d (*No.* NI1)	11·00	☐
	Scotland 3d (*No. S1*)	5·00	☐
	Wales 3d (*No. W1*)	5·00	☐
Sept. 1958	Northern Ireland 6d, 1s 3d (*Nos.* NI3, NI5)	14·00	☐
	Scotland 6d, 1s 3d (*Nos* S3, S5)	12·00	☐
	Wales 6d, 1s 3d (*Nos.* W3, W5)	10·00	☐
une 1964	Guernsey 2½d (*No. 6*)	12·00	☐
	Isle of Man 2½d (*No. 1*)	13·00	☐
	Jersey 2½d (*No. 9*)	12·00	☐
eb. 1966	Guernsey 4d (*No. 8*)	5·00	☐
	Isle of Man 4d (*No. 3*)	5·00	☐
	Jersey 4d (*No. 11*)	5·00	☐
	Northern Ireland 4d (*No.* NI2)	3·00	☐
	Scotland 4d (*No. S2*)	3·00	☐
	Wales 4d (*No. W2*)	3·00	☐
March 1967	Northern Ireland 9d, 1s 6d (*Nos.* NI4, NI6)	1·50	☐
	Scotland 9d, 1s 6d (*Nos.* S4, S6)	1·50	☐
	Wales 9d, 1s 6d (*Nos.* W4, W6)	1·50	☐
Sept. 1968	Guernsey 4d, 5d (*Nos.* 10, 12)	1·00	☐
	Isle of Man 4d, 5d (*Nos.* 5, 7)	1·75	☐
	Jersey 4d, 5d (*Nos.* 12, 14)	1·25	☐
	Northern Ireland 4d, 5d (*Nos.* NI8, NI10)	50	☐
	Scotland 4d, 5d (*Nos.* S9, S11)	50	☐
	Wales 4d, 5d (*Nos.* W9, W11)	50	☐

cimal Issues

uly 1971	Isle of Man 2½p, 3p, 5p, 7½p (*Nos.* 8/11)	3·50	☐
	Northern Ireland 2½p, 3p, 5p, 7½p (*Nos.* NI12/13, NI18, NI23)	4·00	☐
	Scotland 2½p, 3p, 5p, 7½p (*Nos.* S14/15, S20, S25)	4·00	☐
	Wales 2½p, 3p, 5p, 7½p (*Nos.* W13/14, W19, W24)	4·00	☐
Jan. 1974	Northern Ireland 3p, 3½p, 5½p, 8p (*Nos.* NI14/15, NI19, NI24)	1·50	☐
	Scotland 3p, 3½p, 5½p, 8p (*Nos.* S16/17, S21, S26)	1·50	☐
	Wales 3p, 3½p, 5½p, 8p (*Nos.* W15/16, W20, W25)	1·50	☐

6 Nov. 1974	Northern Ireland 4½p, (*No.* NI17)	1·00	☐
	Scotland 4½p (*No. S19*)	1·00	☐
	Wales 4½p (*No. W18*)	1·00	☐
14 Jan. 1976	Northern Ireland 6½p, 8½p (*Nos.* NI21, NI25)	60	☐
	Scotland 6½p, 8½p (*Nos.* S23, S27)	60	☐
	Wales 6½p, 8½p (*Nos.* W22, W26)	60	☐
20 Oct. 1976	Northern Ireland 10p, 11p (*Nos.* NI27, NI30)	1·00	☐
	Scotland 10p, 11p (*Nos.* S29, S32)	1·00	☐
	Wales 10p, 11p (*Nos.* W28, W31)	1·00	☐
18 Jan. 1978	Northern Ireland 7p, 9p, 10½p (*Nos.* NI22, NI26, NI29)	1·00	☐
	Scotland 7p, 9p, 10½p (*Nos.* S24, S28, S31)	1·00	☐
	Wales 7p, 9p, 10½p (*Nos.* W23, W27, W30)	1·00	☐
23 July 1980	Northern Ireland 12p, 13½p, 15p (*Nos.* NI31/3)	2·00	☐
	Scotland 12p, 13½p, 15p (*Nos.* S33/5)	2·00	☐
	Wales 12p, 13½p, 15p (*Nos.* W32/4)	2·00	☐
8 April 1981	Northern Ireland 11½p, 14p, 18p, 22p (*Nos.* NI34, NI38, NI43, NI48)	2·00	☐
	Scotland 11½p, 14p, 18p, 22p, (*Nos.* S36, S40, S44, S47)	2·00	☐
	Wales 11½p, 14p, 18p, 22p (*Nos.* W35, W39, W44, W49)	2·00	☐
24 Feb. 1982	Northern Ireland 12½p, 15½p, 19½p, 26p (*Nos.* NI36, NI40, NI46, NI51)	3·00	☐
	Scotland 12½p, 15½p, 19½p, 26p (*Nos.* S38, S41, S45, S49)	3·00	☐
	Wales 12½p, 15½p, 19½p, 26p (*Nos.* W37, W41, W47, W52)	3·00	☐
27 April 1983	Northern Ireland 16p, 20½p, 28p (*Nos.* NI41, NI47, NI52)	3·00	☐
	Scotland 16p, 20½p, 28p (*Nos.* S42, S46, S50)	3·00	☐
	Wales 16p, 20½p, 28p (*Nos.* W42, W48, W53)	3·00	☐
23 Oct. 1984	Northern Ireland 13p, 17p, 22p, 31p (*Nos.* NI37, NI42, NI49, NI53)	4·50	☐
	Scotland 13p, 17p, 22p, 31p (*Nos.* S39, S43, S48, S51)	5·00	☐
	Wales 13p, 17p, 22p, 31p (*Nos.* W38, W43, W50, W54)	4·50	☐

7 Jan. 1986	Northern Ireland 12p			
	(No. NI35)	1·25 ☐		
	Scotland 12p (No. S37) ..	1·25 ☐		
	Wales 12p (No. W36)	1·25 ☐		
6 Jan. 1987	Northern Ireland 18p			
	(No. NI44)	1·75 ☐		
	Scotland 18p (No. S57)	1·75 ☐		
	Wales 18p (No. W45)	1·75 ☐		
8 Nov. 1988	Northern Ireland 14p, 19p, 23p,			
	32p (Nos. NI39, NI45, NI50,			
	NI54	3·00 ☐		
	Scotland 14p, 19p, 23p, 32p			
	(Nos. S54, S58, S62, S66) ..	3·00 ☐		
	Wales 14p, 19p, 23p, 32p (Nos.			
	W40, W46, W51, W55) ..	3·00 ☐		

POSTAGE DUE STAMPS

PERFORATION. All postage due stamps are perf 14×15

D 1   D 2

1914–23 *Wmk Type* **96** (*Royal Cypher* ('*Simple*')) *sidewa*

D1	D 1	½d	green	..	..	40	40 ☐
D2		1d	red ..	..	..	50	40 ☐
D3		1½d	brown	..	..	32·00	15·00 ☐
D4		2d	black	..	..	50	40 ☐
D5		3d	violet	..	..	2·00	1·00 ☐
D6		4d	green	..	..	18·00	1·75 ☐
D7		5d	brown	..	..	2·50	1·50 ☐
D8		1s	blue	..	..	20·00	2·00 ☐
	Set of 8 ..				..	65·00	20·00 ☐

1924–31 *Wmk Type* **107** (*Block* G v R) *sideways*

D10	D 1	½d	green	..	..	30	30 ☐
D11		1d	red ..	..	..	50	30 ☐
D12		1½d	brown	..	..	26·00	15·00 ☐
D13		2d	black	..	..	1·60	40 ☐
D14		3d	violet	..	..	2·00	40 ☐
D15		4d	green	..	..	12·00	2·00 ☐
D16		5d	brown	..	..	21·00	25·00 ☐
D17		1s	blue	..	..	6·00	75 ☐
D18	D 2	2s 6d	purple/*yellow*	...		40·00	1·75 ☐
	Set of 9 ..	..	..	..	..	£100	42·00 ☐

1936–37 *Wmk Type* **125** (E 8 R) *sideways*

D19	D 1	½d	green	..	..	5·50	5·00 ☐
D20		1d	red ..	..	..	1·00	1·60 ☐
D21		2d	black	..	..	7·50	5·00 ☐
D22		3d	violet	..	..	1·60	1·60 ☐
D23		4d	green	..	..	12·00	15·00 ☐
D24a		5d	brown	..	..	12·00	15·00 ☐
D25		1s	blue	..	..	7·50	4·50 ☐
D26	D 2	2s 6d	purple/*yellow*	..		£160	8·00 ☐
	Set of 8 ..	..	..	..	..	£180	55·00 ☐

1937–38 *Wmk Type* **127** (G vi R) *sideways*

D27	D 1	½d	green	..	..	7·00	3·25 ☐
D28		1d	red ..	..	..	1·75	40 ☐
D29		2d	black	..	..	1·75	40 ☐
D30		3d	violet	..	..	8·00	40 ☐
D31		4d	green	..	..	45·00	7·50 ☐
D32		5d	brown	..	..	7·00	1·00 ☐
D33		1s	blue	..	..	48·00	75 ☐
D34	D 2	2s 6d	purple/*yellow*	..		55·00	1·50 ☐
	Set of 8 ..	..	..	..	..	£150	13·50 ☐

1951–52 *Colours changed and new value* (1½d). *Wmk Ty*
127 (G vi R) *sideways*

D35	D 1	½d	orange	..	..	1·75	2·00 ☐
D36		1d	blue	..	..	1·10	75 ☐
D37		1½d	green	..	..	1·75	1·75 ☐
D38		4d	blue	..	..	22·00	9·00 ☐
D39		1s	brown	..	..	26·00	4·00 ☐
	Set of 5 ..	..	..	..	..	48·00	16·00 ☐

54–55 Wmk Type 153 (Mult. Tudor Crown and E 2 R) sideways

0	D 1	½d orange	.. ..	3·00	2·50	☐	☐
1		2d black	.. ..	1·90	2·00	☐	☐
2		3d violet	.. ..	40·00	25·00	☐	☐
3		4d blue	.. ..	15·00	16·00	☐	☐
4		5d brown	.. ..	17·00	6·50	☐	☐
5	D 2	2s 6d purple/*yellow* ..		£120	3·00	☐	☐
		Set of 6 ..	.. ..	£175	50·00	☐	☐

55–57 Wmk Type 165 (Mult. St Edward's Crown and R) sideways

6	D 1	½d orange	.. ..	1·50	2·25	☐	☐
7		1d blue	.. ..	4·00	1·25	☐	☐
8		1½d green	.. ..	3·75	3·75	☐	☐
9		2d black	.. ..	35·00	3·00	☐	☐
0		3d violet	.. ..	4·50	1·25	☐	☐
1		4d blue	.. ..	18·00	3·00	☐	☐
2		5d brown	.. ..	27·00	3·00	☐	☐
3		1s brown	.. ..	65·00	1·25	☐	☐
4	D 2	2s 6d purple/*yellow* ..		£160	7·50	☐	☐
5		5s red/*yellow*	.. ..	90·00	19·00	☐	☐
		Set of 10 ..	.. ..	£375	40·00	☐	☐

59–63 Wmk Type 179 (Mult. St Edward's Crown) sideways

6	D 1	½d orange	.. ..	10	45	☐	☐
7		1d blue	.. ..	10	15	☐	☐
8		1½d green	.. ..	90	1·50	☐	☐
9		2d black	.. ..	1·25	30	☐	☐
0		3d violet	.. ..	40	15	☐	☐
1		4d blue	.. ..	40	20	☐	☐
2		5d brown	.. ..	45	45	☐	☐
3		6d purple	.. ..	60	30	☐	☐
4		1s brown	.. ..	1·40	25	☐	☐
5	D 2	2s 6d purple/*yellow* ..		4·00	45	☐	☐
6		5s red/*yellow*	.. ..	7·50	70	☐	☐
7		10s blue/*yellow*	.. ..	9·00	3·75	☐	☐
8		£1 black/*yellow* ..		45·00	7·00	☐	☐
		Set of 13	.. ..	60·00	14·00	☐	☐

68–69 Design size 22½ × 19 mm No wmk

9	D 1	2d black	..	40	40	☐	☐
0		3d violet	.. ..	25	40	☐	☐
1		4d blue	.. ..	25	40	☐	☐
2		5d orange-brown	..	4·50	5·25	☐	☐
3		6d purple	.. ..	80	60	☐	☐
4		1s brown	.. ..	80	1·00	☐	☐
		Set of 6 ..	.. ..	6·50	7·00	☐	☐

68–69 Design size 21½ × 17½ mm No wmk

5	D 1	4d blue	.. ..	5·00	5·00	☐	☐
6		8d red	.. ..	1·25	75	☐	☐

3

D 4

Decimal Currency

1970–77 No wmk

D77	D 3	½p turquoise-blue		5	20	☐	☐
D78		1p reddish purple		8	12	☐	☐
D79		2p myrtle-green ..		8	12	☐	☐
D80		3p ultramarine ..		12	10	☐	☐
D81		4p yellow-brown ..		15	15	☐	☐
D82		5p violet		20	20	☐	☐
D83		7p red-brown ..		35	45	☐	☐
D84	D 4	10p red		30	20	☐	☐
D85		11p green		50	60	☐	☐
D86		20p brown		60	50	☐	☐
D87		50p ultramarine ..		1·50	40	☐	☐
D88		£1 black		2·75	60	☐	☐
D89		£5 orange-yellow and black ..		13·00	2·00	☐	☐
		Set of 13		18·00	5·00	☐	☐
D77/82, D84, D86/8 Presentation Pack		.. ..		10·00		☐	
D77/88 Presentation Pack		.. ..		6·00		☐	

D 5

D 6

1982 No wmk

D 90	D 5	1p lake		5	5	☐	☐
D 91		2p bright blue	..	5	8	☐	☐
D 92		3p deep mauve	..	5	15	☐	☐
D 93		4p deep blue ..	..	8	20	☐	☐
D 94		5p sepia ..	..	8	20	☐	☐
D 95	D 6	10p light brown	..	15	25	☐	☐
D 96		20p olive-green	..	30	30	☐	☐
D 97		25p deep greenish blue		40	70	☐	☐
D 98		50p grey-black	..	75	1·00	☐	☐
D 99		£1 red		1·50	80	☐	☐
D100		£2 turquoise-blue ..		3·00	2·00	☐	☐
D101		£5 dull orange ..		7·50	1·50	☐	☐
		Set of 12		12·50	6·50	☐	☐
		Set of 12 Gutter Pairs ..		30·00		☐	
		Presentation Pack		14·00		☐	

ROYAL MAIL POSTAGE LABELS

These imperforate labels were issued as an experiment by the Post Office. Special microprocessor controlled machines were installed at post offices in Cambridge, London, Shirley (Southampton) and Windsor to provide an after-hours sales service to the public. The machines printed and dispensed the labels according to the coins inserted and the buttons operated by the customer. Values were initially available in $\frac{1}{2}$p steps to 16p and in addition, the labels were sold at philatelic counters in two packs containing either 3 values (3$\frac{1}{2}$, 12$\frac{1}{2}$, 16p) or 32 values ($\frac{1}{2}$p to 16p).

From 28 August 1984 the machines were adjusted to provide values up to 17p. After 31 December 1984 labels including $\frac{1}{2}$p values were withdrawn. The machines were taken out of service on 30 April 1985.

Machine postage-paid impression in red on phosphorised paper with grey-green background design. No watermark. Imperforate.

1984 (1 May–28 Aug)
Set of 32 ($\frac{1}{2}$p to 16p)	..	28·00	30·00 □ □
Set of 3 (3$\frac{1}{2}$p, 12$\frac{1}{2}$p, 16p)	..	4·00	4·50 □ □
Set of 3 on First Day Cover			
(1 May)			6·50 □
Set of 2 (16$\frac{1}{2}$p, 17p)			
(28 August)		3·00	3·50 □ □

OFFICIAL STAMPS

Various Stamps of Queen Victoria and King Edward *
Overprinted in Black.

I.R.	I. R.	O.W.
OFFICIAL	OFFICIAL	OFFICIA
(O 1)	(O 2)	(O 3)

ARMY	ARMY	GOVT PARCEL
OFFICIAL	OFFICIAL	
(O 4)	(O 5)	(O 7)

BOARD OF EDUCATION	R.H. OFFICIAL	ADMIRALT OFFICIA
(O 8)	(O 9)	(O 10)

1 Inland Revenue

Overprinted with Types O 1 or O 2 (5s, 10s, £1)

1882–1901 *Queen Victoria*

O 1	52	$\frac{1}{2}$d	green	.. ..	10·00	3·00 □
O 5		$\frac{1}{2}$d	blue	.. ..	25·00	15·00 □
O13	67	$\frac{1}{2}$d	vermilion	..	1·10	40 □
O17		$\frac{1}{2}$d	green	..	3·00	2·25 □
O 3	57	1d	lilac	.. ..	1·00	65 □
O 6	64	2$\frac{1}{2}$d	lilac	.. ..	£110	35·00 □
O14	70	2$\frac{1}{2}$d	purple on blue		50·00	4·00 □
O 4	43	6d	grey	.. ..	75·00	20·00 □
O18	75	6d	purple on red	..	£100	20·00 □
O 7	65	1s	green	.. ..	£2500	£450 □
O15	78	1s	green	.. ..	£200	20·00 □
O19		1s	green and red	.	£600	£100 □
O 9	59	5s	red	.. ..	£1300	£400 □
O10	60	10s	blue	..	£2250	£475 □
O11	61	£1	brown (Wmk Crowns) ..		£18000	□
O12		£1	brown (Wmk Orbs) ..		£22000	□
O16		£1	green	.. ..	£3500	£450 □

20	79	½d blue-green	15·00	1·50	☐	☐
21		1d red	10·00	70	☐	☐
22	82	2½d blue	£400	60·00	☐	☐
23	79	6d purple ..	£85000	£65000	☐	☐
24	89	1s green and red	£500	65·00	☐	☐
25	91	5s red ..	£4000	£1300	☐	☐
26	92	10s blue ..	£15000	£9500	☐	☐
27	93	£1 green ..	£12000	£6000	☐	☐

Office of Works

Overprinted with Type O 3

1896–1902 Queen Victoria

31	67	½d vermilion	90·00	40·00	☐	☐
32		½d green ..	£150	75·00	☐	☐
33	57	1d lilac ..	£150	40·00	☐	☐
34	74	5d dull pur & bl	£750	£150	☐	☐
35	77	10d dull pur & red	£950	£225	☐	☐

1902–03 King Edward VII

36	79	½d blue-green	£350	80·00	☐	☐
37		1d red	£350	80·00	☐	☐
38	81	2d green and red	£600	75·00	☐	☐
39	82	2½d blue ..	£700	£100	☐	☐
40	88	10d purple and red	£5000	£1500	☐	☐

Army

Overprinted with Types O 4 (½d, 1d) or O 5 (2½d, 6d)

1896–1901 Queen Victoria

41	67	½d vermilion ..	1·10	50	☐	☐
42		½d green	1·75	3·00	☐	☐
43	57	1d lilac ..	1·00	50	☐	☐
44	70	2½d purple on blue	4·00	2·00	☐	☐
45	75	6d purple on red	13·00	8·00	☐	☐

Overprinted with Type O 4

1902 King Edward VII

48	79	½d blue-green	1·75	65	☐	☐
49		1d red	1·25	55	☐	☐
50		6d purple	60·00	30·00	☐	☐

Government Parcels

Overprinted with Type O 7

1883–1900 Queen Victoria

69	57	1d lilac ..	25·00	8·00	☐	☐
61	62	1½d lilac ..	£100	25·00	☐	☐
65	68	1½d purple and green	12·00	2·00	☐	☐
70	69	2d green and red	45·00	7·00	☐	☐
71	73	4½d green and red ..	£100	75·00	☐	☐
62	63	6d green ..	£750	£275	☐	☐
66	75	6d purple on red	25·00	10·00	☐	☐
63	64	9d green ..	£625	£175	☐	☐
67	76	9d purple and blue	55·00	15·00	☐	☐
64	44	1s brown (Plate 13)	£425	70·00	☐	☐
64c		1s brown (Plate 14)	£725	£110	☐	☐
68	78	1s green ..	£120	70·00	☐	☐
72		1s green and red ..	£160	50·00	☐	☐

1902 King Edward VII

O74	79	1d red	15·00	5·00	☐	☐
O75	81	2d green and red ..	65·00	15·00	☐	☐
O76	79	6d purple	£100	15·00	☐	☐
O77	87	9d purple and blue	£225	50·00	☐	☐
O78	89	1s green and red ..	£350	85·00	☐	☐

5 Board of Education

Overprinted with Type O 8

1902 Queen Victoria

O81	74	5d dull pur & bl ..	£500	£100	☐	☐
O82	78	1s green and red	£950	£375	☐	☐

1902–04 King Edward VII

O83	79	½d blue-green ..	16·00	7·00	☐	☐
O84		1d red	16·00	6·00	☐	☐
O85	82	2½d blue	£500	50·00	☐	☐
O86	85	5d purple and blue	£2000	£950	☐	☐
O87	89	1s green and red ..	£25000	£15000	☐	☐

6 Royal Household

Overprinted with Type O 9

1902 King Edward VII

O91	79	½d blue-green ..	£150	95·00	☐	☐
O92		1d red	£130	85·00	☐	☐

7 Admiralty

Overprinted with Type O 10

1903 King Edward VII

O101	79	½d blue-green ..	9·00	3·00	☐	☐
O102		1d red	5·00	2·50	☐	☐
O103	80	1½d purple and green	60·00	40·00	☐	☐
O104	81	2d green and red ..	£100	50·00	☐	☐
O105	82	2½d blue	£120	40·00	☐	☐
O106	83	3d purple on yellow	£100	35·00	☐	☐

> **Minimum Price.** The minimum price quoted is 5p. This represents a handling charge rather than a basis for valuing common stamps. Where the actual value of a stamp is less than 5p this may be apparent when set prices are shown, particularly for sets including a number of 5p stamps. It therefore follows that in valuing common stamps the 5p catalogue price should not be reckoned automatically since it covers a variation in real scarcity.

BY APPOINTMENT TO
HER MAJESTY THE QUEEN.
STANLEY GIBBONS LTD
PHILATELISTS

STANLEY GIBBONS LTD
GREAT BRITAIN
MAIL ORDER SERVICE

ow can we help you improve your collection?

We offer you a fast, friendly and efficient service backed by a reputation built up over 133 years of dealing.

The range and depth of our stock is renowned world-wide. Most items we can supply to you immediately – always in the highest quality, and of course backed by the Stanley Gibbons guarantee of genuineness.

To help you fill your more expensive gaps we can offer an interest free payment system which spreads the cost for you over three months.

We can also offer you a Budget Plan which will allow you to add to your collection on a regular basis and at a monthly payment rate that you can afford.

Our regular Mail Order clients have the benefit of exclusive discounts and special offers not made available elsewhere.

> For further details of how we can help you just contact Michael Barrell at the address below. If you would also like to order some items from our stock simply use the order form overleaf.

Michael Barrell, Great Britain (Mail Order) Service
399 Strand, London WC2R 0LX
Tel: 01-836 8444   Fax: 01-836 7342

STANLEY GIBBONS LTD
GREAT BRITAIN
MAIL ORDER SERVICE
ORDER FORM

To order simply fill out the form below (continuing on a separate sheet if necessary). along the dotted line and send it with payment details to Michael Barrell at the addr overleaf.

Please note that all items will be supplied at the prices quoted in this Catalogue (sub to being unsold) until 30 April 1990. After this date we will still supply the items wh possible but there may be some price adjustments.

✂ —

To: Stanley Gibbons Ltd Great Britain Mail Order Service, 399 Strand, London WC2R 0

Please send me

SG No.	Condition (u/m, f/u, etc)	£	p	SG No.	Condition (u/m, f/u, etc)	£	p	SG No	Condition (u/m, f/u, etc.)	£

☐ I enclose cheque/PO made payable to Stanley Gibbons Ltd. for £...............

☐ I have paid £.......... into Stanley Gibbons Giro Account No. 586 6006

Total

Postage & Handling (£2 UK, £4 O/S)

Total Order Value

☐ I authorise you to charge my credit card for £...............

Type of card .... (all major cards accepted)   Expiry date

Card No. [ ][ ][ ][ ][ ][ ][ ][ ][ ][ ][ ][ ][ ][ ][ ][ ]   Signature ....

Name .... Address ....

.... Postcode ....

Please allow 14 days for delivery (overseas customers 21 days)

GREAT BRITAIN

1840 - 1950

YOU CANNOT AFFORD TO MISS OUR FREE ILLUSTRATED LIST

1. SELECTED ITEMS SECTION

For the connoisseur and specialist who collects items of quality and rarity. Line Engraved with scarcer Plates and Maltese Crosses, Surface Printed cds used and with Edward VII & George V shades with Certificates.

2. BARGAINS SECTION

Full of hundreds of inexpensive items from a few pounds upwards. Very strong in Line Engraved, Surface Printed & KEVII, from fillers at only 2% of Cat. to fine mint & VFU singles. Lots of unusual pmks, Used Abroad, KGV shades through to QEII Commems.

Whether average or specialist collector, you cannot afford to miss our free list - so write today!

GB POSTAL AUCTION

Our regular GB-only Postal Auction provides the collector with the opportunity to purchase at 'dealer prices'. From Postal History through to QEII varieties, from basic stamps through to major rarities.

FREE CATALOGUE FOR OUR NEXT SALE - AVAILABLE NOW!

WE URGENTLY NEED TO BUY

Fine quality and rare items/collections of Great Britain.
To get the best price it always pays to contact the specialists first, so contact Barry Fitzgerald at 'The Embassy' Today.

WANTS LISTS . . . WANTS LISTS . . . WANTS LISTS . . .

We constantly supply medium to rare items to clients whose collections range from average to Gold Medal standard - so make sure we are aware of you, and whatever your G.B. requirements may be.

Embassy Philatelists

PHILATELIC FEDERATION PTS

MANFIELD HOUSE, (7th Floor)
376 THE STRAND, LONDON WC2R 0LR
Tel: 01-240-1527. VAT No 228 8653 31

FREE STAMPS!

YOUR INVITATION . . .

Complete below to receive a PERSONALISED selection of our GB approvals.

NO OBLIGATION and new applicants will be offered **£10-worth FREE.***

*(Full details with 1st selection)

❶ Tick: GB ☐ Channel I ☐ IOM ☐
❷ **We supply ALL the British Commonwealth as well.** If you want approvals from any Br. C/WIth country just add the names here: _____
_____
_____

❸ **Tick periods of interest:**
All Reigns ☐ (or)
QV ☐ EDVII ☐ GV ☐ GVI ☐
QEII–1970 ☐ QEII–1971–date ☐

❹ **Tick conditions:**
Mint and used ☐ Used only ☐
Mint only ☐ U/M only ☐

❺ **Tick price range per stamp/set:**
to £5 ☐ to £10 ☐ to £25 ☐ to £50 + ☐

❻ **Your name, address and phone No:**
_____
_____
_____
_____

❼ **A reference (or a credit card number):**
_____

YES! Please send selections of approvals tailor-made to my specifications above. I will return if not required and pay for those kept within 10 days. **As a new client I claim £10-worth FREE as offered.** I may cancel at any time.
ALL APPROVALS SUBJECT TO STANDARD CONDITIONS SENT WITH EACH SELECTION.
Under 18's – parents please sign.

Signed: **Date:**

LOOK – NO envelope or stamp needed!
Simply cut out this page, fold in half as shown, tape edge and post **FREEPOST!**

If you'd rather not cut this catalogue, please apply by letter/FAX (or telephone if you have a credit card) or see our full page advert in your stamp magazine.

SUPERB SELECTIONS
View in your own home!

★ **Superior approvals service.** More and more collectors find the R. Warren way the best way to expand their GB collection.

★ **Convenient home approvals** when YOU want them. Inspect, consider, choose – from the **comfort of home.** NO OBLIGATION, NO PRESSURE.

★ **Huge stocks.** Nearly every stamp listed in this catalogue is ALWAYS in stock – mint and used. From the cheapest to the rarest. And all available to look at **BEFORE** you buy.

★ **Keen prices always.** From 1/20th or less of the catalogue value!

★ **Members PTS and UDPA** Years of experience and hundreds and hundreds of customers ensure your satisfaction. Customers order our approvals again and again!

★ **UK's NUMBER ONE approvals service.** Fill in this form to find out why. APPLY TODAY!

CASH WAITING FOR YOU! If it's British, or British Commonwealth, and worth £100 or more, then we're buyers! TOP PRICES PAID FOR ALL BRITISH STAMPS.

NO STAMP REQUIRED IN U.K.

R. Warren Ltd
FREEPOST
Lingfield
Surrey RH7 6ZA
England

Tel: 0342 833413
Fax: 0342 833413

Lightly sellotape this edge

Warwick & Warwick
Highest obtainable prices for private treaty sales, –at no cost to the vendor.

75% Advance and the full balance within three weeks

A big claim. But one that we've proved time and again. What we're offering is a new deal for the seller. The highest obtainable prices for stamps within three weeks – and an immediate 75% advance – all at no cost to the vendor! Here's how we do it. We have a constantly increasing demand from our Private Treaty buyers throughout the world and we, therefore, urgently need to contact sellers of quality material of all types. It could be a good collection, a specialised study, an accumulation of remainders, a few good single items, covers. Postal History lots, a complete stock, a modern mint investment holding – in fact anything to do with philately. We can sell it.

Visits arranged for any property

A unique service, completely free of charge and without obligation. We can arrange to visit sellers within 48 hours anywhere in the country – practically irrespective of the size of value of the property to be sold. All you have to do is get in touch with us.

Free valuation GUARANTEED SALE

It will pay you to sell through Warwick & Warwick's Private Treaty Service because:

1. You obtain the services of professional valuers – each an expert in his field – whose interests are best served by selling your property at the highest obtainable price. It pays to have Warwick & Warwick on your side!

2. We can visit you within 48 hours – anywhere in the country – to arrange the sale of your property, subject to our assessment of its size and value. There's no obligation and no extra charge (although we reserve the right to decline to visit vendors of small properties). Overseas visits can also be arranged.

3. We give you a written valuation telling you exactly how much you will receive for your collection. This valuation is given FREE of any charge or obligation. We maintain a worldwide register of keen buyers covering every type of philatelic property. We have many buyers listed for every unpopular territory and hundreds of buyers for popular countries. We have many buyers capable of spending up to £50,000 and several with over £250,000 available. You can be sure we have a buyer, with money, waiting for your collection.

4. The sale will be completed quickly. As soon as you have approved our valuation, we will advance you – cheque or cash – 75% of the valuation. We GUARANTEE the balance within three weeks. In order to underwrite this guarantee we will even buy, ourselves, at the full valuation with absolutely no deductions. In fact, sales are often completed within two or three days.

5. If you refuse our valuation you owe us nothing except return postage or transport costs. No charge is made prior to sale (except where valuations of smaller properties – £100 or less – are refused when a charge of £5 is made to partly cover administrative costs).

6. There is no commission or other charge payable by the vendor. You receive the full amount tendered in the valuation. The buyer will be charged with all commissions

and any other costs. And, of course, there is no 'unsold' charge. We haven't failed so far – and we don't intend to start now!

Highest prices obtained

Currently the greatest demand is for older high quality British Commonwealth, particularly Australia & States, B.N.A., New Zealand and Pacifics, Western Europe, Japan, USA and, of course, Great Britain. We can obtain very high prices for specialised collections, postal history material and dealers' stocks. Naturally larger properties are the best sellers as international buyers with unlimited funds will be interested.

We can, and do, sell everything. We have hundreds of overseas clients with special requirements and have consistently obtained the highest prices for practically every philatelic holding, even including so-called dead territories like Eastern Europe and South America. We will not refuse to handle any lot because it is unpopular. And we will continue to maintain this unique record for our clients in the future.

What the Vendors say

Thank you for your courteous and efficient service.
Mr. C., Ipswich, Suffolk
Thank you for the prompt manner you have handled the valuation and sale of my stamps. Mr. W., Wimborne, Dorset
I am delighted with your offer. Prof. G., Hong Kong
I trust that our happy association will continue for many years to come Mr. B., London
Astounded and delighted with such services and appraisals.
Mr. D., New Zealand
Thank you for your kind attention. Mr. N., Clydebank
Copies of these have been submitted to the Editor.

We have the buyers– do you have the stamps?

What can we sell for you? Almost everyone connected with stamps has something which is no longer required and can be turned into cash. Think about it for a few minutes – then let us know. You can either send your material to us by registered mail, call and see us at our offices, or write giving details. Or telephone Warwick (0926) 499031 and ask for a member of our specialist valuation staff. Remember we can be with you in 48 hours.
Free transit insurance can be arranged which will give you full cover for your stamps the whole time they are out of your possession. Contact us for details.

Warwick Warwick

Warwick & Warwick Limited,   Established 1958
Private Treaty Department, Chalon House,
2 New Street, Warwick, CV34 4RX,
Telephone: Warwick (0926) 499031.
Overseas vendors should quote our VAT no. 307 5218 76 on the outside of the package.